RECENT RESEARCHES IN THE MUSIC OF THE NINETEENTH AND EARLY TWENTIETH CENTURIES, 29

Johann Nepomuk Hummel

Mozart's *Haffner* and *Linz* Symphonies

Arranged for Pianoforte,
Flute, Violin, and Violoncello

Edited by Mark Kroll

A-R Editions, Inc.

Mozart's *Haffner* and *Linz Symphonies*

Recent Researches in Music

A-R Editions publishes seven series of critical editions, spanning the history of Western music, American music, and oral traditions.

Recent Researches in the Music of the Middle Ages and Early Renaissance
   Charles M. Atkinson, general editor

Recent Researches in the Music of the Renaissance
   James Haar, general editor

Recent Researches in the Music of the Baroque Era
   Christoph Wolff, general editor

Recent Researches in the Music of the Classical Era
   Eugene K. Wolf, general editor

Recent Researches in the Music of the Nineteenth and Early Twentieth Centuries
   Rufus Hallmark, general editor

Recent Researches in American Music
   John M. Graziano, general editor

Recent Researches in the Oral Traditions of Music
   Philip V. Bohlman, general editor

Each edition in *Recent Researches* is devoted to works by a single composer or to a single genre. The content is chosen for its high quality and historical importance, and each edition includes a substantial introduction and critical report. The music is engraved according to the highest standards of production using the proprietary software MusE, owned by MusicNotes, Inc.

For information on establishing a standing order to any of our series, or for editorial guidelines on submitting proposals, please contact:

A-R Editions, Inc.
801 Deming Way
Madison, Wisconsin 53717

800 736-0070 (U.S. book orders)
608 836-9000 (phone)
608 831-8200 (fax)
http://www.areditions.com

Recent Researches in the Music of the Nineteenth and Early Twentieth Centuries, 29

Johann Nepomuk Hummel

Mozart's *Haffner* and *Linz* Symphonies

Arranged for Pianoforte,
Flute, Violin, and Violoncello

Edited by Mark Kroll

A-R Editions, Inc.
Madison

Performance parts are available from the publisher.

A-R Editions, Inc., Madison, Wisconsin 53717
© 2000 by A-R Editions, Inc.

All rights reserved. No part of this book may be reproduced or transmitted in any form by any electronic or mechanical means (including photocopying, recording, or information storage and retrieval) without permission in writing from the publisher.

The purchase of this work does not convey the right to perform it in public, nor to make a recording of it for any purpose. Such permission must be obtained in advance from the publisher.

A-R Editions is pleased to support scholars and performers in their use of *Recent Researches* material for study or performance. Subscribers to any of the *Recent Researches* series, as well as patrons of subscribing institutions, are invited to apply for information about our "Copyright Sharing Policy."

Printed in the United States of America

ISBN 0-89579-466-7
ISSN 0193-5364

∞ The paper used in this publication meets the minimum requirements of the American National Standard for Information Sciences—Permanence of Paper for Printed Library Materials, ANSI Z39.48-1984.

Contents

Acknowledgments vi

Introduction vii
  Background vii
  Johann Nepomuk Hummel vii
  The Arrangements x
  The Editions xiii
  Notes on Performance xiii
  Notes xv

Plates xvii

Symphony in D Major, K. 385 *(Haffner), Wolfgang Amadeus Mozart* 1
  I. Allegro con spirito 1
  II. Andante 20
  III. Minuetto 28
  IV. Finale: Presto 31

Symphony in C Major, K. 425 *(Linz), Wolfgang Amadeus Mozart* 51
  I. Adagio; Allegro spiritoso 51
  II. Poco adagio 73
  III. Menuetto 85
  IV. Finale: Presto 88

Critical Report 115
  Sources 115
  Editorial Methods 115
  Critical Notes 116
  Notes 117

Acknowledgments

I would like to thank my friends and colleagues from Germany, the violinist Waltraut Wächter and the Baroque cellist Thomas Fritzsch. They brought these arrangements to my attention, and we have performed many of them in this country and Europe. Inexpressible gratitude is given to violinist Carol Lieberman, my colleague and wife of thirty years. We have also performed these works together, and recorded the *Haffner* and *Linz* symphony transcriptions, and at this point in our careers we have performed almost all the literature for violin and harpsichord/fortepiano. I am indebted to her for her excellent playing and years of advice and support. Likewise I offer thanks to Baroque flutist John Solum and Baroque cellist Arthur Fiacco, who were part of the abovementioned recording, as well as numerous concert performances, and to Wayne Wadhams of Boston Skyline Records, who had the courage and vision to produce the compact disc. I am very grateful to Professor Wendy Heller of Princeton University for her invaluable advice and assistance. Special thanks to Professor Richard Cornell of Boston University, who spent many hours making a computer generated copy of the *Linz* Symphony, and to Holly Mockovak, Head of the Music Library at Boston University, for her help with microfilms and source material. I also thank Hugh Cobbe, Head of the Music Collections at the British Library, for making the source material available to me, and for the generous approval for its use and reproduction.

Introduction

Background

Composers have always been attracted to the possibilities inherent in transferring musical works from one medium to another, and the art of arrangement has a long and colorful history. For example, vocal music in the sixteenth century often appeared in elaborate keyboard settings, and the rise in chamber and symphonic music in the seventeenth century inspired adaptations from one instrumental scoring to another. Bach and Handel also saw the value in transcriptions, not only as a means of reusing musical material but also of gaining deeper understanding of a composition, and many of their works appear and reappear in different configurations.

The musical and social conditions in the early decades of the nineteenth century created a particularly favorable environment for this practice. There were, of course, no radio, television, or recordings, so an evening spent playing transcriptions was an ideal way for a rapidly growing middle class to learn and enjoy the newest compositions. For those living far from major cultural centers, this might be the only opportunity to "hear" a symphony or concerto. Thus, no sooner had a large orchestral work been premiered or published than an arrangement for small ensemble became available for home use. Sometimes the arrangements appeared *before* the original was heard! Moreover, playing these transcriptions served many purposes. Not only were they a popular form of private entertainment but, at times, an accepted mode of romantic courtship. Composers, entrepreneurs, and sometimes unscrupulous publishers therefore found an eager audience hungry to purchase and play the latest home version of a new orchestral or choral work, and the most renowned figures of the period contributed to the genre. Some of the best examples are these transcriptions by Hummel.

Johann Nepomuk Hummel

Johann Nepomuk Hummel is one of the significant musical figures in the nineteenth century. During his lifetime, he was considered the greatest pianist in Europe, and critics and colleagues often included him among the ranks of Beethoven and Weber as a composer. Hummel was also witness to the transformation from the classical to the romantic styles. Here was a musician who was both an intimate of Mozart and a colleague of Chopin. Yet, his own accomplishments have been largely overshadowed by those of his greater contemporaries, Haydn, Mozart, and Beethoven, and his music is essentially unknown today. It is indeed ironic that he so skillfully served their cause even further by transcribing their masterpieces.

Born in Bratislava on 14 November 1778, he moved with his family to Vienna at some point between 1785 and 1786, when his father Johannes became director of the *Theater auf der Wieden*. Shortly thereafter, father and son visited Mozart in the hope that he would accept the young Nepomuk as a student. Johannes's colorful description of the meeting is worth quoting at length:

> Mozart was hard at work when we entered, but in spite of that he received me with the friendly words, "Ah look; it's my dear Hummel; where have you been, and how are you? It's good to see you. Sit down; and you, my young friend, find yourself a chair." I had to sit down on the sofa next to the little man. "What brings you here?" he then asked me. With some slight embarrassment I brought out my request. He listened to me with patience, but when I had finished he looked a bit doubtful and said, "You know, my dear friend, I don't much like taking on pupils; it takes up too much of my time and disturbs me in my work. But let's see and hear what the boy's like, and whether he's worth helping. Sit down at the piano, then, and show us what you can do," he said to Nepomuk. The latter came out with a few small pieces by Bach which he had carefully practised, and spread them out. Mozart left him alone and he began. Wolfgang had sat down beside me again and listened with his arms crossed. He became ever more still, his expression ever more rapt; his eyes shone more brightly and joyously. During the performance he nudged me gently with his arm a few times and nodded appreciatively towards me.... Suddenly, with a look that sparkled and twinkled for joy, he put his hand on my knee, pressed it gently, and whispered to me, "You must leave the lad here with me. I shan't let him out of my sight—something can be made of him!" ... Mozart got up, hurried over to him, put his hand on his head, and said, "Bravo, bravo; you're a splendid lad. Carry on like that and you'll get on all right!" ... and to me he said, "It's agreed, then, I'll teach the lad, but he must live with me so that I can always have my eye on him. He shall have everything free, lessons, lodging, food. You will not have any of the cares of looking after him. Agreed?" Shortly after, my son Nepomuk moved to Mozart's house, where he was treated like a son of the family. He was as comfortable

and well cared for as possible; Wolfgang looked after him like a father, and Konstanze cared for him like a mother.[1]

Thus was Hummel's career and artistic direction launched. Over thirty years later he would acknowledge the pivotal role this event played in his life, in a letter dated 22 May 1826:

> The development of my talent was originally through my father, who was a good, wide-awake musician, and was advanced from my seventh to around my ninth year under Mozart's instruction.[2]

After these two years of instruction, Mozart, perhaps recalling his own childhood experiences with *his* father, suggested that Johannes take his gifted son on tour. In December of 1788 the pair embarked on a trip which would last five years and take them through Germany, Denmark, The Netherlands, Scotland, and England. The three years they spent in England were especially useful. Nepomuk studied with Clementi, met Haydn, and made valuable life-long connections and friendships. Haydn was obviously impressed by the young prodigy and even asked him to substitute for an indisposed pianist who was to play a concert of Haydn's own works.[3] Hummel must have acquitted himself admirably. Fifteen years later, Haydn would recommend him to the post of Konzertmeister to Prince Nicolaus Esterhazy at Eisenstadt.

Before Eisenstadt, however, Hummel returned to Vienna in 1793, where he devoted his energies to composition studies with Albrechtsberger and Salieri. Hummel finally moved to Esterhazy in 1804, and one of his first official duties was to conduct the first performance in that court of Haydn's *Die Schöpfung*. Haydn was unable to attend but sent a letter expressing his faith in the young conductor's skills.[4]

Hummel left the service of the Prince in 1811 and returned to Vienna, where he earned a living as a freelance teacher, conductor, and composer. He also met Beethoven during this period, and even played timpani (alongside of Meyerbeer!) in a benefit concert of Beethoven's *Wellington's Victory*. Hummel and Beethoven were such contrasting personalities that it should come as no surprise that their relationship fluctuated between warm admiration and open hostility. On one occasion Beethoven asked Hummel to make a piano arrangement of *Fidelio*. When the eager young composer presented the finished work, Beethoven cast it aside in displeasure and gave the commission to Moscheles. Nevertheless, Hummel maintained contact with Beethoven throughout his life. According to Schindler, he rushed to the dying composer's bedside for a tearful reconciliation, and served as a pallbearer at the funeral.[5]

In 1813 Hummel married the singer Elizabeth Röckel, and a year later the first of his two sons was born. With a wife and child to support, Hummel sought and accepted the steady employment of Kapellmeister to the Royal Württemberg Court. Nevertheless, the conditions in Württemberg were not suited to his temperament and needs, and on 12 November 1818 Hummel was dismissed. He was then free to accept a new post in 1819, as Kapellmeister to the grand duke of Saxe-Weimar.

Weimar proved to be an ideal environment for Hummel, and he would remain as Kapellmeister in this city until his death on 17 October 1837. Here Hummel had frequent contact with important and interesting artists, foremost among them being Goethe, and his three-month guaranteed leave allowed considerable freedom to tour as a pianist. Hummel traveled widely and established his reputation throughout Austria, Poland, Russia, The Netherlands, France, and England. During these tours, he met such figures as Chopin in Poland and John Field in Russia, and achieved particular success in England.

As Europe's leading pianist, Hummel was admired for his virtuoso technique, unflappable facility, and beautiful tone, qualities like those of his teacher Mozart. Chopin referred to Hummel as being one of the "Masters we all recognize."[6] The commentator Edward Holmes wrote that "In cantabile and scale passages, Hummel's playing seems to have greatly resembled that of his Master—Mozart."[7] In the 1830s the British pianist Charles Salaman remarked that Hummel played "with ease and tranquil, concentrated power; undeviating accuracy, richness of tone and delicacy of touch."[8] Weber added his approbation: "His playing is extraordinarily sure, neat and pearly, as well as elegant."[9]

A review in the English journal *The Athaeneum* reflected the prevailing opinion of Hummel's skills. After hearing "Hummel's Concert" of 29 April 1830, they wrote:

> We had on Thursday the gratification of hearing, for the first time, the pianist who has long been spoken of as the greatest of his time. Hummel's style of playing appears to us decidedly that of Cramer; there is the same perfection of finish—the same classical attention to time—the same delicacy and elegance of ornament, always appropriate—never superfluous. With all these attributes of excellence, there is, in addition, so much more force and energy, that on the whole we certainly regard it as the most sensible and best, consequently the most effective, pianoforte performance we have ever heard.[10]

Czerny himself compared Hummel favorably with Beethoven, praising Nepomuk's "purity of detail, elegance and tenderness," while describing Beethoven's playing as being of "an unholy strength, characterful, with unheard of bravura."[11]

As accomplished as his playing must have been, it was as an improviser that Hummel was perhaps without peer. Many of his concert programs have survived, and most concluded with an "Improvisation by Hummel."[12] Numerous eyewitnesses expressed astonishment and rapture. On one occasion, Ludwig Spohr described an evening in which Hummel was accompanying dancers at a waltz. Hummel started simply enough, but soon began to improvise, first playing in free fantasy, then adding a fugue and finally closing in the galant style, while all the time preserving the waltz rhythm.[13] The American pianist Louis Moreau Gottschalk likewise reminisced:

So exceptional was Hummel as an extemporizor that during a concert in the Erard Hall, Paris, when bells from a nearby church began ringing, he was able to switch immediately from his Polonaise *La bella capricciosa*, Opus 55, into a harmonization of the peal, which he then combined with motifs from the Larghetto Introduzione, capping the whole with a fugue improvised on the main theme of the polacca.[14]

Moscheles was also a close friend and admirer of Hummel, but he did make this honest entry in his diary after an evening of dinner and improvisation on 26 October 1832, at which Mendelssohn was also present: "Hummel, however, I felt, was no Felix."[15]

Yet Hummel's primary responsibilities at Weimar were as a conductor. He presided over performances at the court chapel and conducted the operas presented at the court theater. These included Gluck's *Iphigénie en Aulide*, *Iphigénie en Tauride*, and *Alceste*; Mozart's *Don Giovanni*, *Die Zauberflöte*, *Le nozze di Figaro*, *La clemenza di Tito*, *Così fan tutte*, and *Die Entführung aus dem Serail*; Cherubini's *Médée* and *Lodoïska*; Spontini's *La vestale*; Méhul's *Joseph*; Catel's *Sémiramis*; Salieri's *Axur*; Sacchini's *Oedipe à Colone*; Beethoven's *Fidelio*; and some of the earliest performances of Weber's *Der Freischütz*. His formidable energy was acknowledged by the *Chronik des Weimarischen Hoftheaters*, which reported on 3 April 1819 that he had "conducted the fiftieth performance in Weimar of Mozart's *Don Giovanni*."[16]

In addition to all of these duties, Hummel was also a much sought-after teacher. The leading pianists of the day, such as Sigismond Thalberg, Ferdinand Hiller, Adolf von Henselt, and Carl Czerny, all flocked to Weimar to work with him. The fruit of his teaching, and one of his most important legacies, is the monumental treatise, *A Complete Theoretical and Practical Course of Instructions, on the Art of Playing the Piano Forte*.[17] This seminal work appeared in German, English, and French at approximately the same time. It contains invaluable information about piano playing and performance practice in the nineteenth century and had a profound effect on the future development of the piano and pianists well into the twentieth century.

The treatise is divided into three parts. The first answers basic technical questions, such as the proper manner of sitting at the piano, principles of reading music, etc. Part two provides a comprehensive study of fingering. The third part is the most valuable for the purposes of today's performers. Divided into two sections, Hummel first offers instructions on the execution of ornaments. In the second section, appropriately titled in the French edition "La Belle Execution," he provides perceptive commentary and advice on the aesthetics of piano playing, such as touch, style, pedaling, and improvisation.

The treatise is therefore an important source for the performance of the music of Hummel and this period, and today's performer would be wise to consult it frequently. To cite just one example, Hummel discusses the use of pedals in detail. Hummel obviously preferred to employ the pedals less frequently than his contemporaries. They are to be used with discretion, and primarily in slow movements. Hummel writes:

> Though a truly great Artist has no occasion for Pedals to work upon his audience by expression and power, yet the use of the damper-pedal, combined occasionally with the piano-pedal (as it is termed), has an agreable [sic] effect in many passages, its employment however is rather to be recommended in slow than in quick movements, and only where the harmony changes at distant intervals: all other Pedals are useless, and of no value either to the performer or to the instrument.[18]

He also makes perceptive observations on the difference between English and German pianos, and his observations are very useful for artists who are fortunate enough to be able to play on either style of instrument, originals or copies. Hummel writes:

> Piano-fortes, generally speaking, are constructed on two different plans, the *German* or *Vienna*, as it is termed, and the *English*; the former is played upon with great facility as to touch, the latter with considerably less ease.... It cannot be denied that each of these mechanisms has its peculiar advantages. The German piano may be played upon with ease by the weakest hand. It allows the performer to impart to his execution every possible degree of light and shade, speaks clearly and promptly, has a round fluty [sic] tone, which in a large room contrasts well with the accompanying orchestra, and does not impede rapidity of execution by requiring too great an effort.

Hummel, the frugal "burgher," adds this comment:

> These instruments are likewise durable, and cost but about half the price of the English piano-forte.

He continues, somewhat gingerly, in order not to insult his English publisher and audience:

> To the English construction however, we must not refuse the praises due on the score to its durability and fullness of tone. Nevertheless this instrument does not admit of the same facility of execution as the German; touch is much heavier, the keys sink much deeper, and, consequently, the return of the hammer upon the repetition of a note, cannot take place so quickly.

Hummel's no-nonsense advice is typically solid and practical (and ever diplomatic), reflecting his years of experience as a touring pianist:

> Whoever is yet unaccustomed to these instruments, should not allow himself to be discomposed by the deep descent of the keys, nor by the heaviness of the touch; only let him not hurry himself in the time, and let him play all quick passages and runs with the usual lightness of finger; even passages which require to be executed by strength, must, as in the German instruments, be produced by the power of the fingers, and not by the weight of the arms; for as this mechanism is not capable of such numerous modifications as to degree of tone as ours, we gain no louder sound by a heavy blow, than may be produced by the natural strength and elasticity of the fingers.[19]

As a person, Hummel stands in marked contrast to the conventional stereotype of the temperamental artist of the period. He seems to have been a faithful husband and father, a solid "burgher" who loved his house and famous garden. His priorities for home and hearth can be seen in a letter to Peters of 29 November 1823: "I am also of a mind now to enjoy my lovely house, and therefore I wish to make no trips next year, but rather to remain in Weimar."[20] As Weber succinctly described, Hummel was "a good simple fellow, without pretension and conceit."[21] Carl Czerny offers this description:

> For several years (c. 1801–04) my father and I visited Mozart's widow; every Saturday there were musical soirées at her house.... On one occasion the party was a good bit larger than usual, and among the many elegant persons I was especially fascinated by a very striking young man. His unpleasant, common-looking face, which twitched constantly, and his utterly tasteless clothing (a light-gray coat, a long scarlet vest, and blue trousers) seemed to indicate that he was some village schoolmaster. But the many valuable diamond rings he wore on almost all fingers provided a most peculiar contrast. As usual there was music, and finally this young man (he might have been somewhat older than twenty) was asked to play. And what an accomplished pianist he turned out to be! Even though I had already had so many opportunities to hear Gelinek, Lipavski, Wolfl, and even Beethoven, the playing of this homely fellow seemed like a revelation. Never before had I hard [sic] such novel and dazzling difficulties, such cleanness and elegance in performance, nor such intimate and tender expression, nor even so much good taste in improvisation.[22]

Hummel was also an astute businessman. His extensive correspondence reveals little about the man or artist, but is primarily concerned with financial matters, copyrights, and commissions. Hummel was well known for his vigilance about money, and at the time of his death his estate was valued at more than eighty times that of his annual salary.

Hummel's collaboration with the British businessman and amateur musician George Thomson allows us a revealing glimpse into Hummel's character as well as the state of musical and business affairs in Europe at that time. Thomson was a senior clerk of the Board of Trustees for the Encouragement of Art and Manufacturers in Scotland. An avid collector of Scottish, Irish, and Welsh tunes, he commissioned composers such as Haydn, Beethoven, and Pleyel to make arrangements of these song for piano, flute, violin, and cello. His attempts, however, met with limited success, particularly with Beethoven, whose arrangements were always too complicated and difficult for the Scottish market. Thomson expressed his frustration in a letter of 29 August 1821:

> I have no expectation of ever receiving any benefit from what Beethoven has done for me. He composes for posterity; I had hoped that his gigantic genius would bend and accommodate itself to the simple character of national Melodies, but in general he has been too learned and eccentric for my purpose; and all my gold ducats, about 700 of them, have been thrown away, besides the expense of engraving, printing and paper![23]

His collaboration with Hummel was much more felicitous, and the practical German composer provided a number of usable arrangements. Nevertheless, the state of piano playing in Britain during this era must have been truly lamentable, and even Hummel's work seemed to pose too many problems for its musicians. Thomson wrote to Hummel that:

> Our Singers generally accompany their own voice; they are often poor players; and of course are much puzzled if they have too many notes to occupy their fingers, while the song requires so much of their attention.—Some of those which you have obligingly done for me, tho' always masterly, are rather too difficult in the Piano Forte part."[24]

Hummel was obviously surprised by the reaction. His answer was tactful, but unflinchingly honest:

> I was indeed surprised to hear that your Public should find the Symphonies and Accompanyments too difficult, as in our Country they would find them very easy.[25]

Hummel's business acumen, and his preoccupation with finances and position, can be seen in his early negotiations with Thomson, to whom he wrote (with charming syntax and spelling):

> I have only to remark You on this Occasion, that the Price of 4 Ducats is very low for the present circumstances, the composition of distinguished Authors being payd much higher now than before in our Country.... For those reasons I hope, You will do me justice and raise the Honorar something more, when You'll favor me in the future with other airs.[26]

We are fortunate that Thomson raised the "Honorar."

The Arrangements

As we have seen, Hummel was a frequent and welcome visitor to the British Isles. He made three extended tours there after his initial visit as a child and, with the exception of the final tour, they were successful and rewarding. In one sense, Hummel was as famous in England as in Europe, if not more so. It should therefore come as no surprise that the largest number of Hummel's compositions appeared in British editions.

Hummel's publishing success was due in great part to his agent, J. R. Schultz. A German or Austrian, Schultz settled in England in the early part of the century and established himself as an entrepreneur-publisher-musician. He commissioned or published a number of European compositions, including Beethoven's Variations, Op. 121a and Hummel's Trio in E major, Op. 33. C. F. Peters served as the business contact for almost all of Hummel's dealings with Schultz, until Peters's death in 1827.

Arrangements were at the height of their popularity during this period, and Schultz obviously saw in them a large market. Beginning in 1820, he commissioned from Hummel the first of what would eventually comprise more than fifty transcriptions (see table 1). In August of that year he published, with Boosey, Hummel's arrangement of F. H. Himmel's Overture in C minor, in two versions (for piano four-hands and for a trio of piano, violin,

TABLE 1
Arrangements by J. N. Hummel (including locations of publication, publishers, comments, and other sources)

Arrangement	Location	Publisher	Comments	Other
Twelve Select Overtures Prometheus (Beethoven) Die Zauberflöte (Mozart) Lodoïska (Cherubini) Figaro (Mozart) Iphigénie en Aulide (Gluck) Original Overture (Hummel) Sargino (Paer) Original Overture (A. Romberg) Der Freischütz (Weber) Euryanthe (Weber) Tancredi (Rossini) Anacréon (Cherubini)	England	Boosey	Entered in Stationer's Hall, 1 March 1821 (no. 1 only); all others ca. 1821–early 1830s	

Twelve Overtures (second set)
Les deux journées (Cherubini)
Démophon (Vogel)
Il matrimonio segreto
  (Cimarosa)
Opferfest (Winter)
Le calife de Bagdad (Boieldieu)
Don Giovanni ("Don Juan")
  (Mozart)
La clemenza di Tito (Mozart)
Fanchon (Himmel)
Il barbiere di Siviglia (Rossini)
La gazza ladra (Rossini)
L'italiana in Algeri (Rossini)
Fidelio (Beethoven)
	England	Boosey	No entry	

Fidelio (Beethoven) for piano four-hands	Vienna	Artaria	ca. 1814	
Beethoven, *Septet*	England	Birchall etc., "for the proprietor" (J. R. Schultz?)	Entered in Stationer's Hall, 28 August 1827	
Beethoven, *Symphonies* No. 1, Op. 21 No. 2, Op. 36 No. 3, Op. 55 No. 4, Op. 60 No. 5, Op. 67 No. 6, Op. 68 No. 7, Op. 92	England	Chappell	Entered in Stationer's Hall:* "No. 1," 14 September 1825 "No. 2," 26 April 1826 "No. 6," 17 May 1832 "No. 5," no entry "No. 3," 10 August 1827 "No. 4," 17 February 1829 "No. 7," 1 December 1835	France —— —— Schott Schott, ca. 1830 Schott, Dépôt, 2 May 1827 Schott, ca. 1829 Schott, ca. 1835
Haydn, *Symphonies* No. 44 No. 100 No. 102 No. 103	England	"For the proprietor; sold by S. Chappell"	Entered in Stationer's Hall: "No. 4," no entry "No. 1," 25 May 1832 "No. 2," 18 August 1832 "No. 3," 10 June 1835	Breitkopf & Härtel No date 1832 1832 No date
F. H. Himmel, *Overture in C-minor* (arranged for piano four-hands and for piano, violin, and cello)	England	Boosey	Entered in Stationer's Hall, August 1820 (both versions)	Peters (no date)

TABLE 1 (CONTINUED)

Arrangement	Location	Publisher	Comments	Other
Mozart, *Concerti for Piano and Orchestra*	England	Chappell	Entered in Stationer's Hall:	Schott
No. 10, K. 316a			"No. 3," no entry	1 February 1830
No. 18, K. 456			"No. 7," no entry	MS, January 1830
No. 20, K. 466			"No. 1," no entry	27 August 1828
No. 22, K. 482			"No. 6," no entry	1836–37
No. 24, K. 491			"No. 4," no entry	1831–32
No. 25, K. 503			"No. 2," no entry	10 January 1829
No. 26, K. 537			"No. 5," 1 December 1835	——
Mozart, *Symphonies*	England	"For the proprietor" (J. R. Schultz), by Goulding, Chappell	Entered in Stationer's Hall:	Schott (possibly pirate)
No. 35, K. 385			"No. 5," 10 August 1824	
No. 36, K. 425			"No. 4," 10 August 1824	
No. 38, K. 504			"No. 1," 8 August 1823	
No. 39, K. 543			"No. 3," 10 August 1824	
No. 40, K. 550			"No. 2," 8 August 1823	
No. 41, K. 551			"No. 6," 8 August 1823	
A. Romberg, *Symphony in D*	England	Chappell	17 February 1829	Schott, Bibliothèque de la France, 28 March 1829
Scottish Songs	England			Thomson, nos. 1–5, 1826

*Numbers in quotation marks are those assigned to the published arrangements and/or cited in publication entries.

and cello). Peters also published an edition of these works in Germany. During the next ten years Hummel would arrange symphonies and concertos by Mozart, Haydn, and Beethoven, the Beethoven Septet, and twenty-four opera overtures. He scored them all for piano, flute, violin, and cello, and all were written for London.

Hummel was clearly the right choice for such commissions. He was, after all, Mozart's most famous student, Europe's renowned pianist, and a friend and colleague of Beethoven and Haydn. He had also conducted many of the pieces he would now arrange.[27] Furthermore, Hummel's personality was particularly well-suited to the task. He was a consummate craftsman and a reliable businessman who did not let his ego interfere with the regular production of such seemingly mundane "Gebrauchsmusik." The income they produced must have also pleased Hummel. The transcriptions, which probably took little time or effort, were extremely lucrative. For example, he received eight pounds and fifteen shillings for each overture and more for the larger pieces.

This should not imply that the transcriptions are not of the highest quality, or that Hummel did not apply himself with sensitivity and artistic responsibility. To the contrary, unlike the vast majority of arrangements produced by an industry of second-rate "hacks," Hummel's are masterpieces of the genre. Being so familiar with the originals (and the composers), he had a complete understanding of the music and style. Through his transcriptions we can see how a great artist viewed his even greater contemporaries. Furthermore, they represent an historical gold mine, yielding invaluable insights into the performing practices of the time. For example, Hummel frequently added metronome markings and other performance indications (such as dynamics, slurs, etc.) which reflected his intimate knowledge of actual performances of the music, perhaps by the composers themselves. His metronome markings in particular shed light on the controversial questions of historical tempi.[28] In the case of the Mozart piano concerti, he felt free to make alterations to the scores, including new cadenzas and ornamentation. These reveal how Hummel (or Mozart) himself performed them, or how they might have been played by the current generation of pianists.[29]

The Editions

The state of music publishing in the nineteenth century was complicated and byzantine at best, and chaotic or illegal at worst. Unauthorized or pirate editions appeared almost simultaneously with official publications, and composers were generally at the mercy of unscrupulous publishers. The modern editor is therefore faced with some formidable obstacles in establishing the date of a composition or its publication, or in choosing an authoritative source or edition. Some of the major publishers of the period were Peters, Schott, and Breitkopf & Härtel in Germany; Haslinger in Austria; Schlesinger in Berlin and Paris; Erard and Farrenc in Paris; and Chappell, Birchall, and Boosey in England. For a comprehensive and thorough understanding of this complex situation, the reader is urged to consult Joel Sachs's excellent work on the subject.[30]

The ever-vigilant Hummel was acutely aware of the problems in publishing, and he led the efforts to establish some form of copyright protection for composers. Yet even Hummel was not immune to the predatory practices of these publishers. From a letter of 18 August 1825 to Schlesinger we learn of his displeasure that Schlesinger had printed his arrangement of Beethoven's Symphony no. 1 in Paris without his permission; perhaps Schultz had sold him the rights without Hummel's knowledge.[31] Hummel particularly disliked Schlesinger (as did almost everyone else), and he subsequently chose to have Schott publish his future works in France (even though he had once called Schott and Simrock "the two awful German note-thieves from Mainz and Bonn").[32] In France Hummel also worked with Erard and Hanry, but preferred dealing with the relative newcomer Aristide Farrenc. Hummel also worked often with Breitkopf & Härtel. He asked them to publish his first three Haydn symphony arrangements before Schultz.[33] Furthermore, Breitkopf & Härtel had bought the rights for Germany for Hummel's arrangements of four Haydn symphonies in 1832, but three years later they declined to take a fifth, since the original four had not sold well.

Despite the machinations of the publishers, Hummel was not to be easily trifled with. He was well aware of his eminent stature and considerable influence in the musical community, and a publisher would anger or deceive him at his peril. In one instance he wrote to Peters that Schultz had better "learn to recognize with whom he is dealing!"[34]

As we have seen, Hummel had more stable and collegial dealings with Peters in Germany, and their voluminous correspondence reveals a good working relationship. Peters had published the first Himmel arrangement simultaneously with Boosey, obviously with Hummel's blessings. From that point on, Hummel tried to maintain a practice of dual and simultaneous publications in England and Germany, obviously in order to enhance his royalties and to protect against piracy. The arrangements of Beethoven's symphonies and Mozart's piano concerti were also published in France and Germany by Schott. Chappell and Boosey had the rights in England to all of the arrangements.

The editor's task is not made any easier by public advertisements or inclusion in music catalogues such as *Whistlings Handbuch*, since these might list both an official edition and a piracy with equal sanction. The establishment of the "German Music Publisher's Union" would go a long way to rectify this situation.

The conditions in England were somewhat more stable and easily understood. Once again, Sachs has written extensively on the subject. To summarize briefly, English copyright law required that a publisher deposit one or more copies of a new work at Stationer's Hall in London. After such a deposit, the work would receive its certification and copies would be made for national and university libraries. Therefore, since no composition was allowed to be "entered at Stationer's Hall" without having demonstrated proof of ownership, this certification should give a reasonable assurance that the volume was not a piracy.

However, the system was hardly foolproof, and one cannot use the records in the Stationer's Hall with complete equanimity. Publishers might not deposit their works at all, or the high costs of depositing would deter them from entering more than one work in a series of compositions. This was the case with Hummel's first set of *Twelve Select Overtures*. Only the first overture was officially deposited, perhaps on the assumption that the deposit and its protection would apply to the other eleven overtures.

Notes on Performance

Hummel's indications for dynamics, phrasing, and articulation are quite clear and unambiguous, and can be followed with confidence. There are, however, instances in which identical passages played by two or more instruments are notated with a different phrasing and/or dynamic.[35] This should not be a source of confusion. The practice of non-uniform phrasing during the eighteenth and nineteenth centuries was much more common than is usually assumed; by this, composers sought to achieve variety in color and musical texture. Today's performer should therefore avoid the temptation to smooth over these supposed "irregularities" by imposing a uniformity in all parts.

Likewise, the scoring of a passage might have a different dynamic in each of the four instruments. Here Hummel achieves subtle differences in dynamics, and also distinguishes between principal or solo material and secondary or accompanying figures.

Questions about the realization of ornaments, choices of fingering, or, for that matter, most issues of execution can be easily answered by going directly to the source. That is, consult Hummel's own treatise frequently.

Hummel provides metronome markings for each movement, except the last of the *Haffner*. These certainly indicate his personal preference, but perhaps might also reflect Hummel's recollection of Mozart's own tempi for his symphonies. It is not improbable that Hummel heard Mozart conduct these works, or studied them with the master himself. For this reason alone, the metronome markings provide invaluable historical information regarding original tempos.[36]

However, performers who follow these markings will find some tempi unreasonably fast, and at times almost unplayable (particularly for the pianist!) In such instances, the performer must keep in mind that a metronome marking was merely intended as a guide or "starting point" and as an indication of the character of a work. The composer never expected that this number would be followed mechanically, in an unyielding and automatic manner. As in all good musical performance, tempo should be adjusted throughout a movement to reflect changes in character, texture, and musical context. Hummel, Beethoven, and other commentators were aware of the danger of being a slave to the metronome at the expense of the music. For example, in the autograph of his song "Nord oder Süd," Beethoven wrote that a metronome marking can apply "to only the first measures, for feeling also has its tempo and this cannot entirely be expressed in this figure."[37] Hummel himself writes in the treatise that "Many persons still erroneously imagine, that, in applying the metronome, they are bound to follow its equal and undeviating motions throughout the whole piece, without allowing themselves any latitude in the performance for the display of taste and feeling."[38]

Hummel adds no pedal indications in the piano part, but this should not be surprising. After reading his treatise, as well as contemporary accounts of his playing, it is clear that he used the pedal with discretion. However, once again this should not prevent the performer from adding pedal for expressive purposes, or as an adjustment to a particular piano or acoustical space, or simply in a passage where he believes that the addition of pedal would enhance the musical meaning or expression. On the other hand, there are also instances in which Hummel instructs the pianist to hold the sustaining pedal much longer than one would expect, through many measures in which the harmonies change frequently. Although this is contrary to the teachings of modern piano pedaling, this was also a common practice during this period. The effect can be quite dramatic, especially when played on pianos of the period.

Regarding the choice of actual instruments, and particularly the piano, it is instructive to look at the resources available when these transcriptions appeared. The typical Viennese-style piano of the period 1820–30 (as represented by builders such as Graf, Walther, and Dulcken) had six or six and a half octaves, and could be fitted with a variety of pedals and special devices. These would usually include a sustaining pedal, an *una corda* (in which only one of three strings would be struck), and a *sordine* (to mute the sound by means of a cloth or other material placed on the strings). Pianos also had *due corda* pedals, which struck two strings rather than three, and special-effect pedals such as the *janissary*, which operated a drum and triangle built into the instrument. English instruments were equally large and complex, the best being made by Broadwood, and typically had six or six and a half octaves and a full complement of pedals and devices. However, it is useful to remember that these transcriptions were primarily intended for home use, and were most often played on instruments built for the typical middle class household. A piano was part of the basic furnishings for any self-respecting bourgeois home in the early nineteenth century. These instruments were usually smaller square pianos, such as those ubiquitous house instruments built by Clementi & Co. in London or the "Nachttisch" (table) squares of Germany, but larger upright models such as the "giraffe" or "pyramid" piano were also popular.

The flutes in Hummel's time were made with a forest of materials, including boxwood, ebony, and ivory, and could have from one to eight keys. Theobald Boehm began his groundbreaking work on the flute in 1832. His conical bore and ingenious design transformed the instrument and established what is now the modern flute. The violin and cello would have been fitted with gut strings. A chin rest for the violin or an end-pin for the cello were still optional, although becoming more typical, and the bow was of the early modern Tourte style. The prevailing pitch of the time would have fallen within the range of $a' = 427–30$ cycles per second. However, there was really no standard diapason "a," and pitch varied from country to country, and even from city to city. Performers fortunate enough to play on instruments of the period will learn a great deal from the experience and find the realization of these works quite natural and satisfying. However, needless to say, performance on a modern piano, flute, violin, and cello is an equally valid and acceptable approach to this repertoire.

Moreover, these works can also be performed on piano alone. Publishers were quite aware that a pianist living in a small village, far from a major city, might not have a full ensemble of instrumentalists to accompany him. Not to ignore this market, publishing houses offered for sale solo piano versions of many of the transcriptions. For example, in 1825 Schott published Hummel's transcription of Mozart's Symphony K. 543 in solo piano format. Hofmeister similarly published a solo edition of Hummel's arrangement of the *Linz* Symphony K. 425 around the same time. Since the bulk of the musical material was already contained in the piano part, a solo version would not compromise the integrity of the work, and made practical business sense.

Notes

1. From Otto Erich Deutsch, *Mozart: A Documentary Biography*, trans. Eric Blom, Peter Branscombe, and Jeremy Noble (Palo Alto: Stanford University Press, 1965), 569–70. According to Deutsch, the account first appeared in an article by Moritz Müller, "Ein alter Musikmeister," in the periodical *Europa* (Leipzig, 1873), no. 37.

2. Karl Benyovsky, *J. N. Hummel, Der Mensch und Künstler* (Bratislava: Eos, 1934), 199. All translations of material from this book are my own. The original German is: "Die Entwicklung meines Talentes wurde anfangs durch meinen Vater, der ein guter Musiker war, gewekt, und von meinen 7ten bis zum 9. Jahr durch Mozart's Unterricht befördert."

3. Benyovsky, *J. N. Hummel*, 42.

4. H. C. Robbins Landon and Dénes Bartha, *Joseph Haydn: Gesammelte Briefe und Aufzeichnungen* (Bärenreiter: Kassel, 1965), 451. Haydn wrote (from Vienna, on 26 September 1804):
Liebster Hummel
Bedaure von Herzen, dass ich das vergnügen nicht haben kan, mein kleines Werck zum letztenmal selbst zu Dirigiren; indessen ober bin überzeugt, dass sich alle (keinesausgenohmen) die mühe geben werden Ihren alten Papa nach Kräften zu unterstützen, besonders da Sie den verdienstvollen Hummel zum Anführer haben.
[Dearest Hummel, With heartfelt regrets I cannot have the pleasure to conduct my little work myself for the last time. However, I am convinced your old Papa will be supported with every (without exception) effort, especially since [he has] the deserving Hummel as the leader.]

5. Charlotte Moscheles, *Aus Moscheles' Leben*, 2 vols. (Leipzig: Duncker und Humbolt, 1872–73), reprinted as Ignatz Moscheles, *Recent Music and Musicians* (New York: Da Capo Press, 1970), 100–101. Alan Tyson, however, reports that Hummel lobbied Beethoven at his death bed to support his efforts to establish a system of copyright laws. Although less dramatic and romantic, this version seems more in keeping with Hummel's character. Cited in Alan Tyson, "Steps to Publication—and Beyond," in *The Beethoven Companion* (London: Faber and Faber, 1971), 461.

6. *Selected Correspondence of Fryderyk Chopin*, ed. Bronislaw Edward Sydow (New York: McGraw-Hill, 1963), 24.

7. Edward Holmes, *The Life of Mozart* (London: Chapman and Hall, 1845), 257.

8. As cited in Marion Phyllis Barnum, "J. N. Hummel and His Treatise on Piano Playing" (D.M.A. diss., University of Iowa, 1971), 40.

9. As quoted in Benyovsky, *J. N. Hummel*, 67–68. "Sein Spiel ist ausserordentlich sicher, nett und geperlt, auch zuweilen elegant."

10. *The Athaeneum*, 1 May 1830, 269–70.

11. Cited in Barnum, "J. N. Hummel and His Treatise on Piano Playing," 37.

12. Sample programs from the Paris tour of 1825, as cited by Joel Sachs, "Hummel in England and France" (Ph.D. diss., Columbia University, 1968), 8–9, are as follows. 15 April, 8:00 P.M.: (1) Quintette, composed by Hummel, played by him with MM. Videil, Sina, Norblin, Lami; (2) Air, sung by Mme. Pasta; (3) Solo for French horn, composed and played by M. Dauprat; (4) Novelle sonate for piano and 'cello ("encore manuscrite"), played by Hummel and Norblin; (5) Duo, composed by Rossini, sung by Mme. Pasta and M. Pellegrini; (6) Improvisation by Hummel. 22 April, 8:00 P.M.: (1) Sonata, piano four-hands, composed by Hummel, played by Hummel and Kalkbrenner; (2) Air, sung by Mme. Marconi-Schonberger; (3) Variations for mandoline, played by M. Vimercati; (4) Terzette by Paer, sung by Mlle. Dorus, Mme. Marconi-Schonberger, M. Levasseur; (5) Trio, composed by Hummel, played by him with MM. Baillot and Norblin; (6) Air, sung by Mlle. Dorus; (7) Improvisation by Hummel.

13. Louis Spohr, *Selbstbiographie* (Kassel und Göttingen, 1860), 1:206. See also Benyovsky, *J. N. Hummel*, 172.

14. Cited in Robert Stevenson, "Gottschalk in Western South America," Inter-American Music Bulletin, no. 74 (Washington, D.C.: Organization of American States, Division of Cultural Relations, Nov. 1969), 13.

15. Moscheles, *Recent Music and Musicians*, 184.

16. Benyovsky, *J. N. Hummel*, 90.

17. German edition: *Ausführliche theoretisch practische Anweisung zum Pianoforte Spiel vom ersten Elementar-unterricht an bis zur vollkommensten Ausbildung* (Vienna: T. Haslinger, 1828). French edition: *Méthode complète theorétique et practique pour le pianoforte* (Paris: A. Farrenc, 1829).

18. Hummel, *A Complete Theoretical and Practical Course of Instructions, on the Art of Playing the Piano Forte* (London: T. Boosey, [ca. 1827]), 62.

19. Hummel, *A Complete Theoretical and Practical Course of Instructions*, 64–65.

20. Benyovsky, *J. N. Hummel*, 229. "Ich bin auch gesonnen nun mein hübsches Haus zu genießen, und will daher nächstes Jahr keine Reise machen sondern in Weimar bleiben."

21. Cited in Barnum, "J. N. Hummel and His Treatise on Piano Playing," 35.

22. Cited in Barnum, "J. N. Hummel and His Treatise on Piano Playing," 27.

23. From a letter to the poet William Smyth (1765–1849) of 29 August 1821 (British Museum, Add. 35,268, fols. 57–58). Also cited in Joel Sachs, "Hummel and George Thomson of Edinburgh," *The Musical Quarterly* 61 (1970): 271.

24. Thomson to Hummel, 29 October 1831 (British Museum, Add. 32,188, fols. 1–2). Also cited in Sachs, "Hummel and George Thomson of Edinburgh," 285.

25. Hummel to Thomson, 2 February 1830 (British Museum, Add. 35,265, fol. 214). Also cited in Sachs, "Hummel and George Thomson of Edinburgh," 282.

26. Hummel to Thomson, 1 June 1826 (British Museum, Add. 35,265, fols. 165–66). Also cited in Sachs, "Hummel and George Thomson of Edinburgh," 276.

27. Sachs writes, in "Authentic English and French Editions of J. N. Hummel," *Journal of the American Musicological Society* 25 (1972): 209 no. 30, that "Hummel conducted at least fifteen of the twenty-four overtures he arranged: *Die Zauberflöte, Figaro, Iphigénie en Aulide, Der Freischütz, Euryanthe, Tancredi, Anacreon, Il Matrimonio segreto, Opferfest, Don Giovanni, La Clemenza di Tito, Fanchon, Il Barbiere di Siviglia, L'Italiana in Algeri,* and *Fidelio.* In addition, he conducted the "Jupiter" Symphony, a Symphony by Haydn in E♭, which could have been No. 103, and Beethoven Nos. 3, 5, and 6 (and 8, which he did not live long enough to arrange). All the preceding performances were at Weimar; he may have conducted other works on tours."

28. For a complete discussion of the issue of metronome markings and tempi, see Robert Münster, "Authentische Tempi zu den sechs lezten Sinfonien W. A. Mozarts?" *Mozart-Jahrbuch* (1962/63): 185–99.

29. Sachs writes, in "Authentic English and French Editions of J. N. Hummel," 209–10 n. 30, that "Although Hummel played Mozart concertos as a child, there is no evidence that he ever performed any after returning to Vienna in 1793." Still, contemporary commentators "constantly spoke of Hummel's arrangements as being valuable aids to study. I found two instances of the concerto arrangements being performed:

Königsberg, winter of 1834/35, Concerto in C minor, by a dilettante; Berlin, January 27, 1830, concert in honor of Mozart's birthday, Concerto in D minor played by a Hummel student, Wenzeslaw Hauck."

30. See especially his articles, "Authentic English and French Editions of Hummel" and "Hummel and George Thomson of Edinburgh" in *JAMS* and *MQ*, respectively, as well as his dissertation, "Hummel in England and France" (all cited previously).

31. See Benyovsky, *J. N. Hummel*, 233–34.

32. In a letter to Peters, dated 29 November 1823, Hummel writes "von den beiden schlechten deutschen Notendieben aus Mainz und Bonn," as quoted in Benyovsky, *J. N. Hummel*, 229.

33. Cited in Sachs, "Hummel in England and France," 190 n. 1.

34. Cited in Sachs, "Hummel in England and France," 189 n. 1. "Schultz mag dafür auch ein wenig zapeln, damit er besser einsehen lernt, mit wem er es bei mir zu thun hat."

35. For example, in m. 19 of the Andante movement in the *Haffner* Symphony transcription, the violin and piano play the same notes, but are given different articulations. A parallel passage in m. 68 of the same movement confirms Hummel's intentions.

36. For an interesting discussion of this subject, see Münster, "Authentische Tempi zu den sechs lezten Sinfonien W. A. Mozarts?"

37. See *Thayer's Life of Beethoven*, rev. and ed. Elliot Forbes (Princeton: Princeton University Press, 1967), 2:687–88.

38. Hummel, *A Complete Theoretical and Practical Course of Instructions*, 65.

Plate 1. Johann Nepomuk Hummel, *Mozart's Six Grand Symphonies, Arranged for the Piano Forte with Accompaniments of Flute, Violin, & Violoncello* (London, 1824), *Haffner* Symphony, flute part, first page of Allegro con spirito. Courtesy of the British Library.

Plate 2. Johann Nepomuk Hummel, *Mozart's Six Grand Symphonies, Arranged for the Piano Forte with Accompaniments of Flute, Violin, & Violoncello* (London, 1824), Linz Symphony, piano part, first page of Poco adagio. Courtesy of the British Library.

Symphony in D Major, K. 385 *(Haffner)*

I

Wolfgang Amadeus Mozart

2

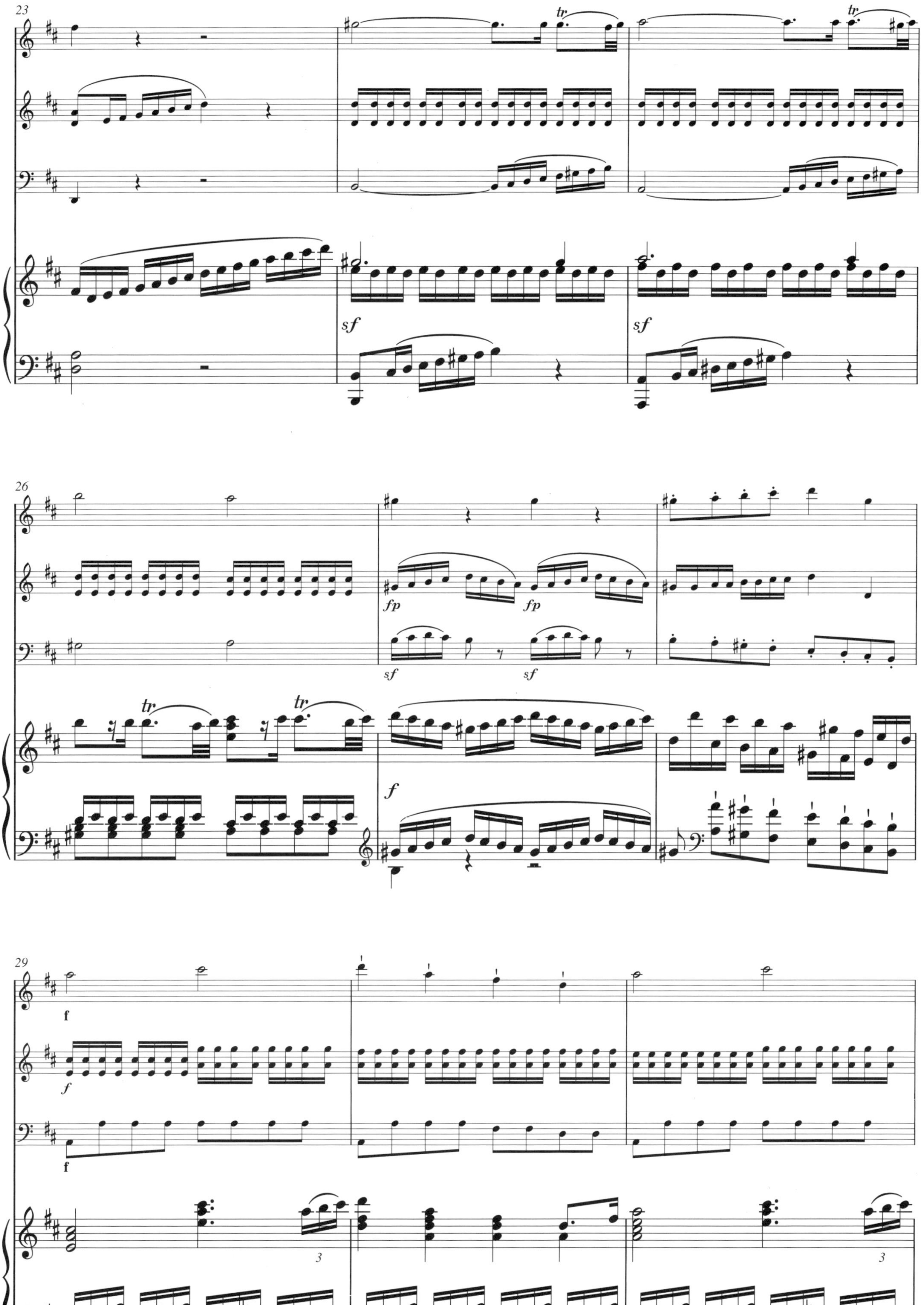
23
tr
tr
sf
sf
26
tr
tr
fp
fp
sf
sf
f
29
f
f
f
3
3

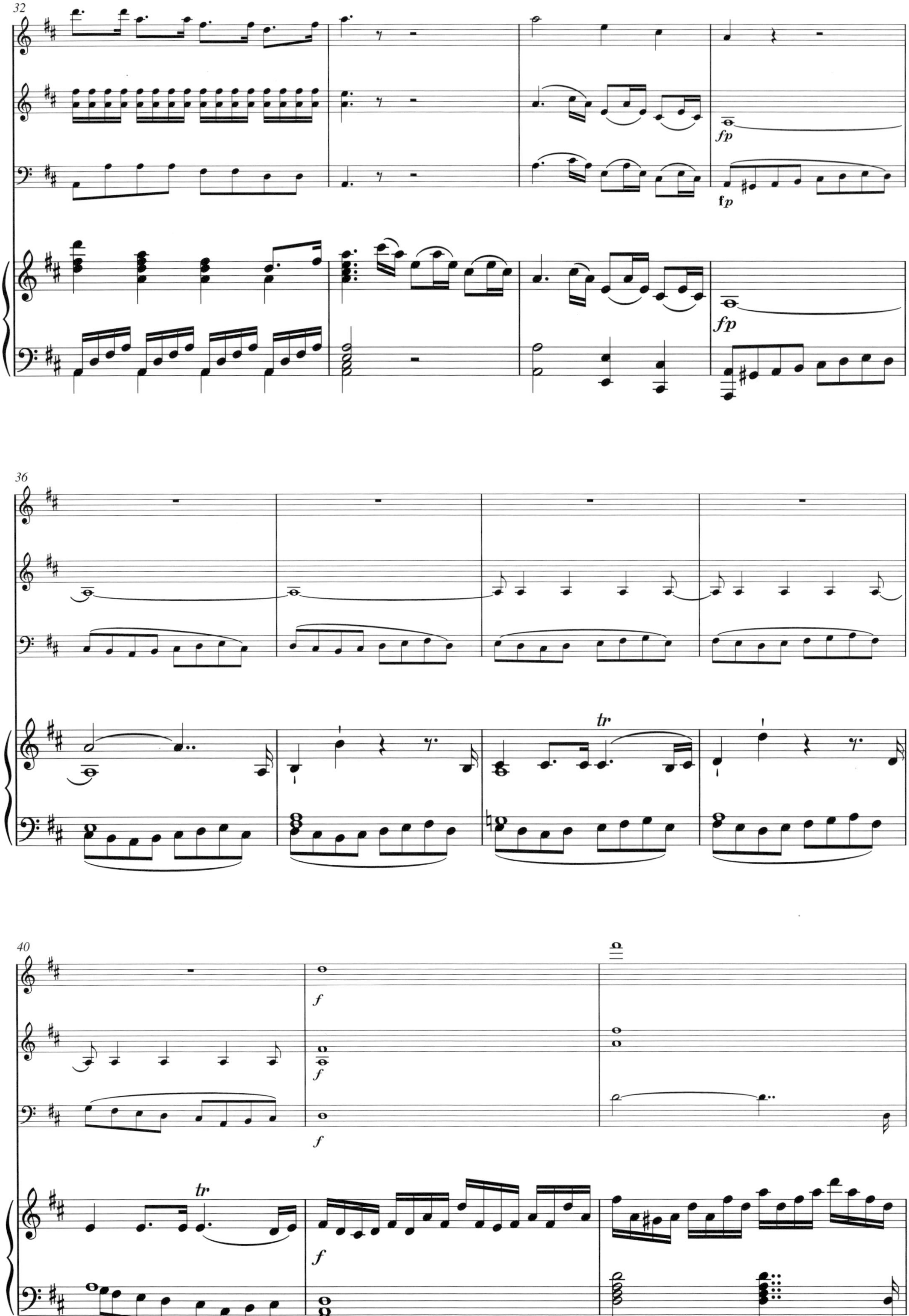

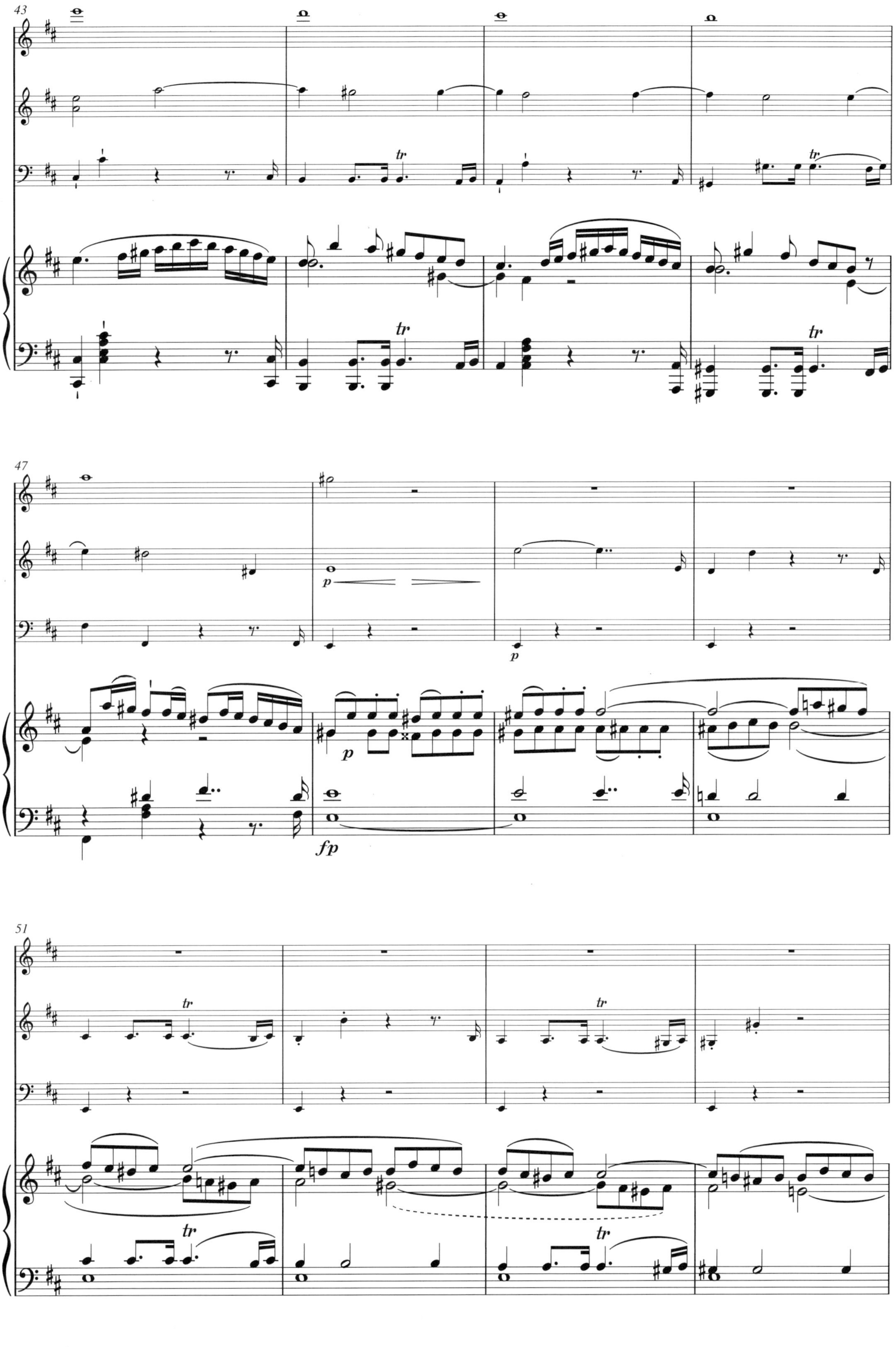
43
47
51

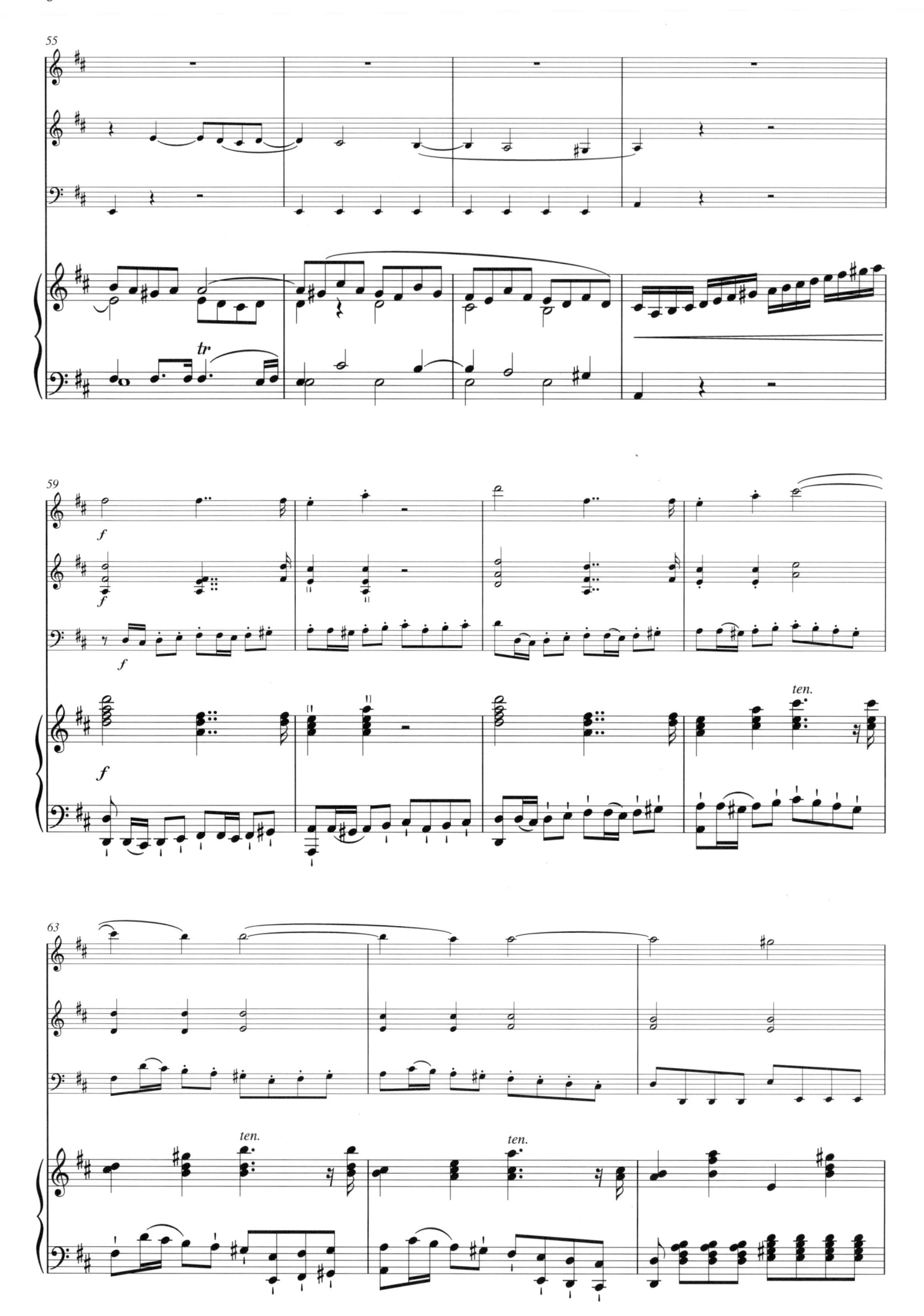
55
tr
59
f
f
f
f
ten.
63
ten.
ten.

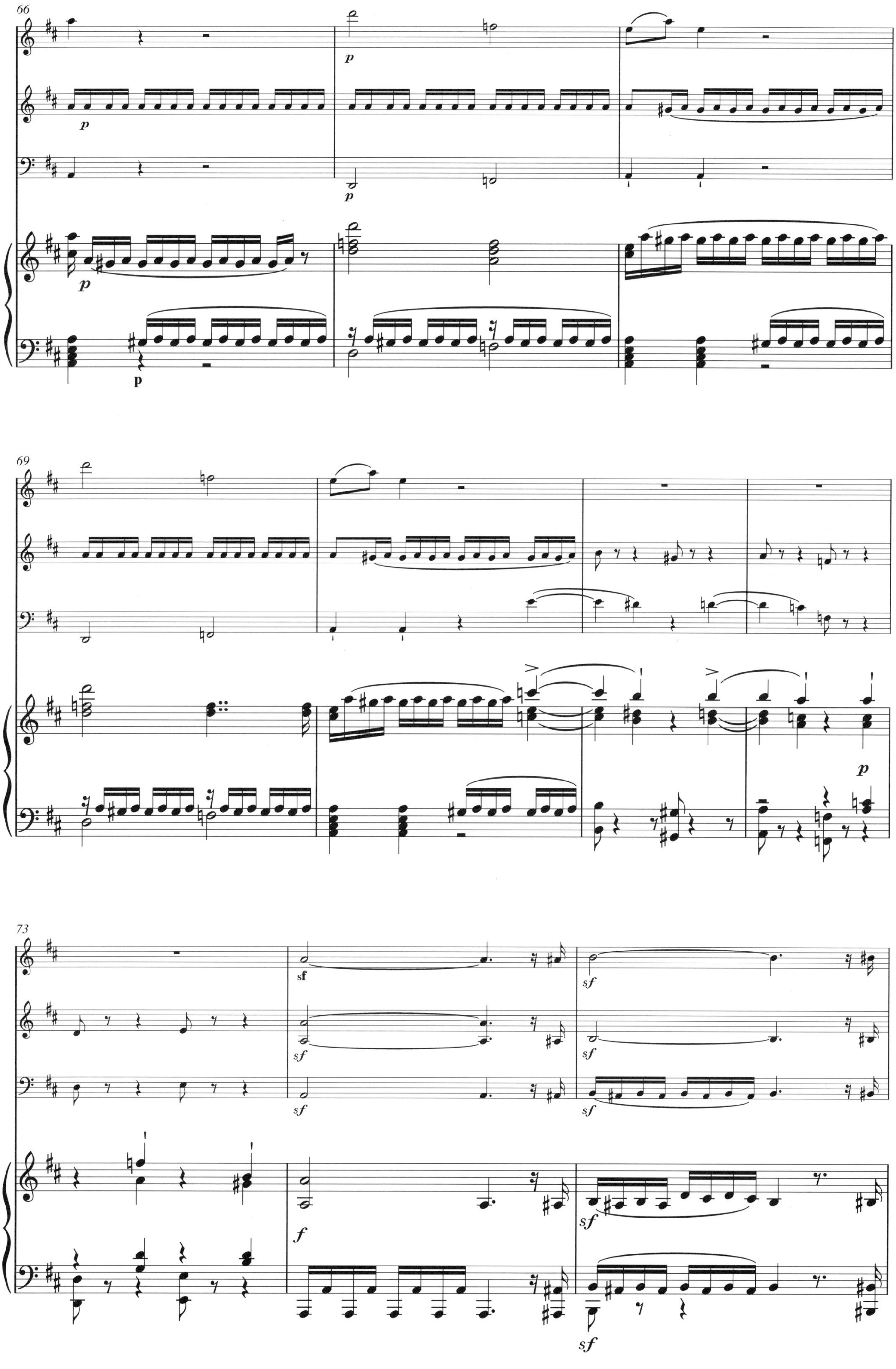
66
69
73

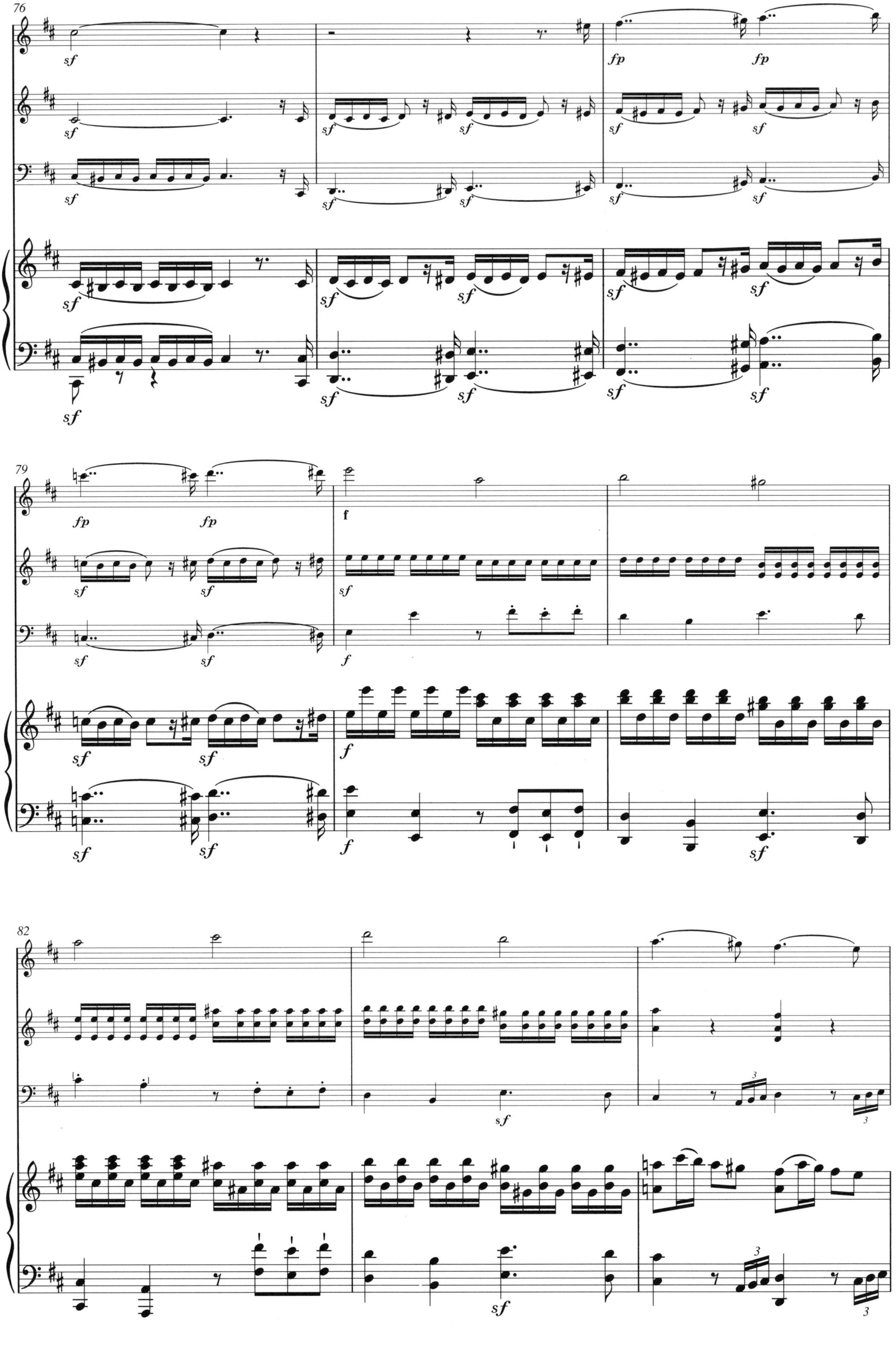
76
79
82

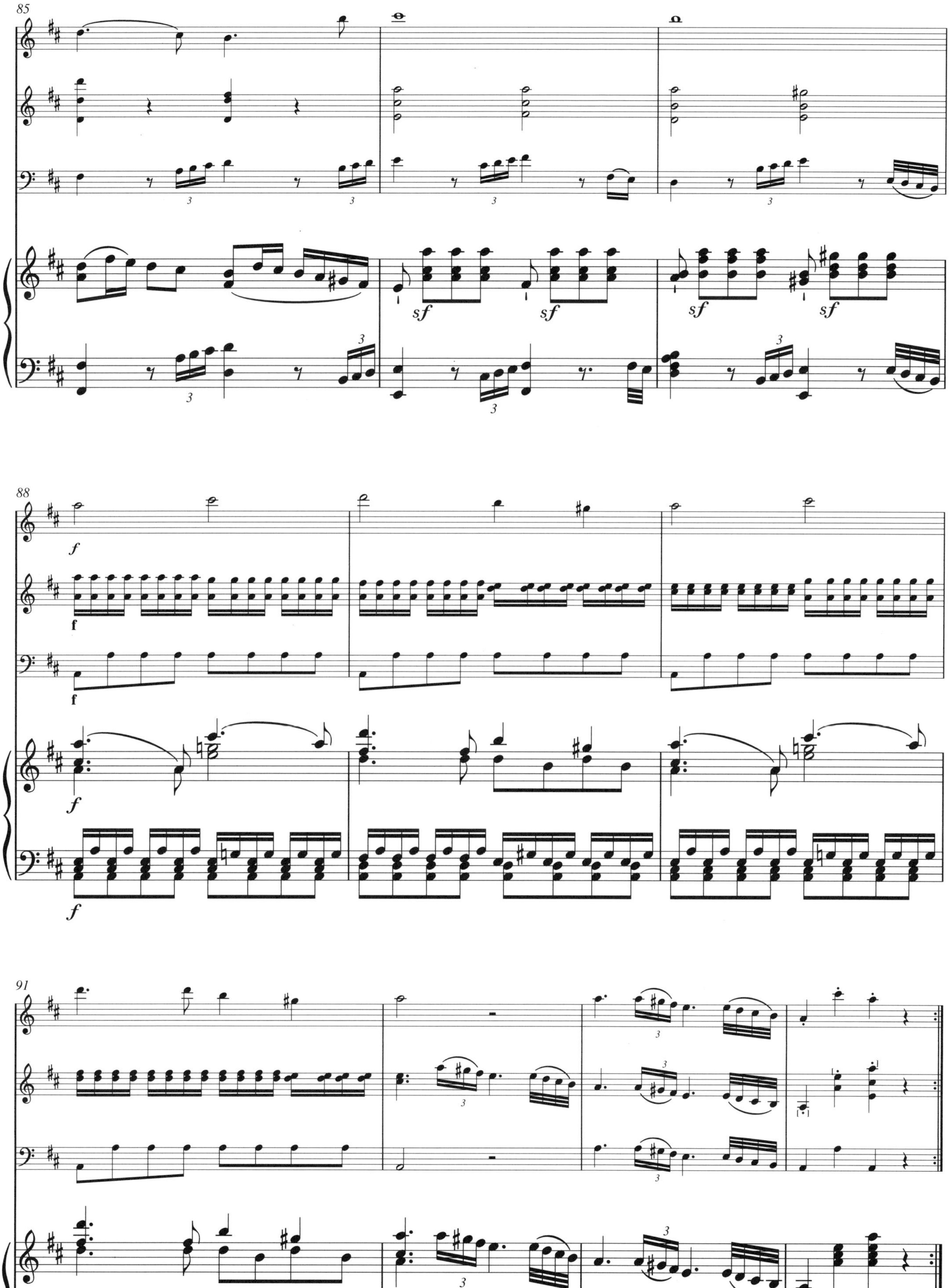
85
sf
88
f
91

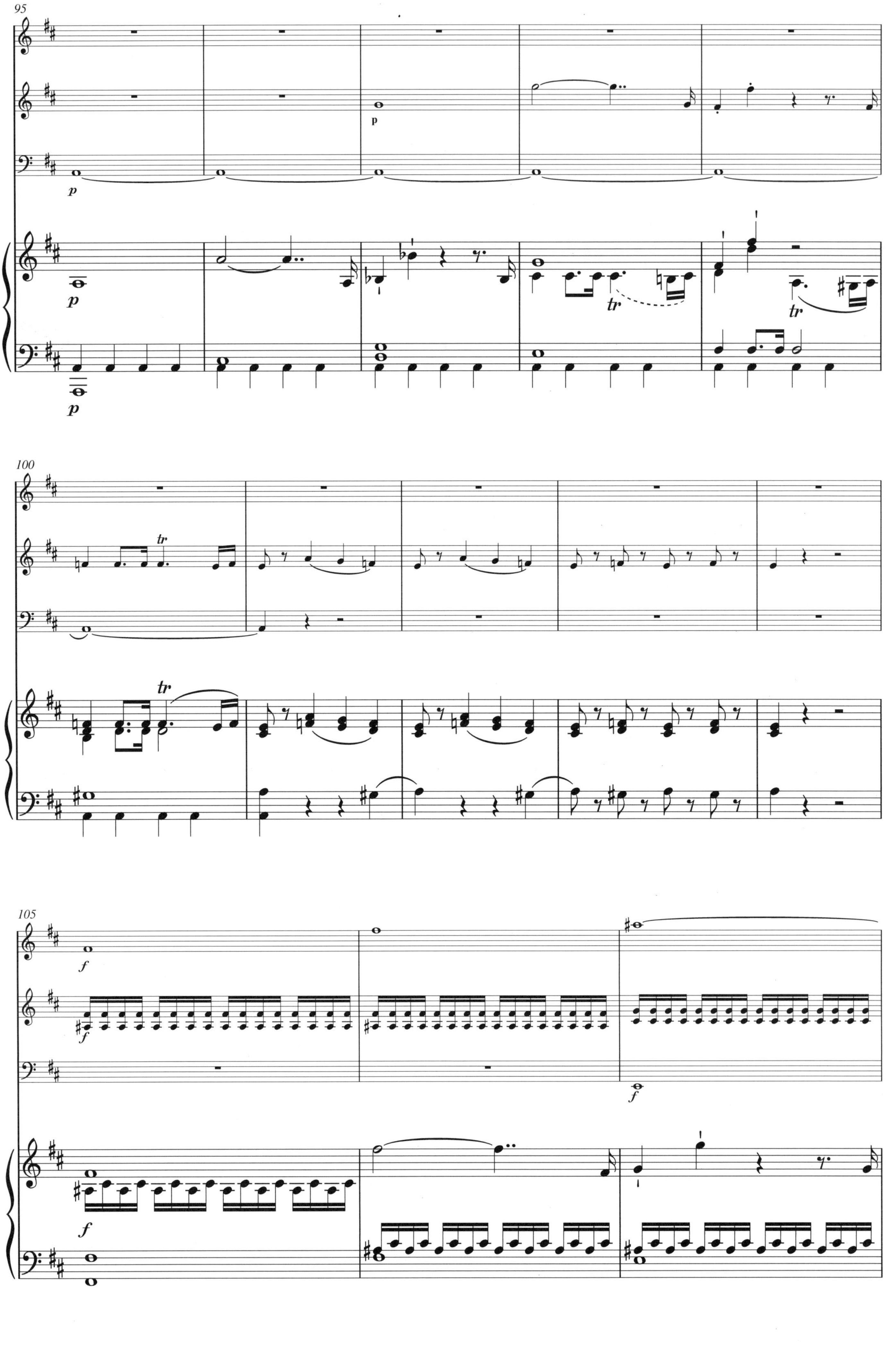
95
100
105

11

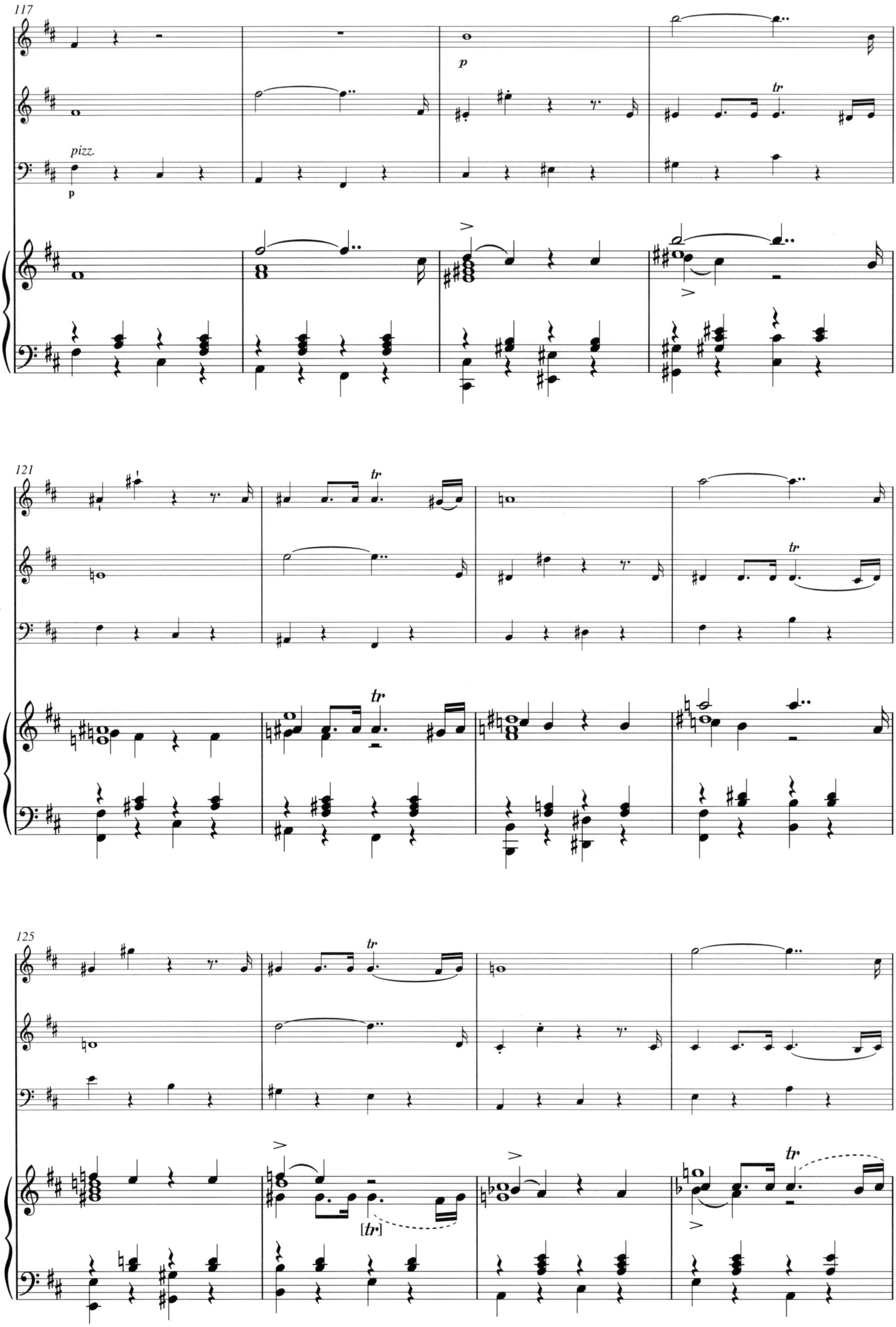
117
pizz.
p
p
tr
121
tr
tr
tr
125
tr
tr
[tr]

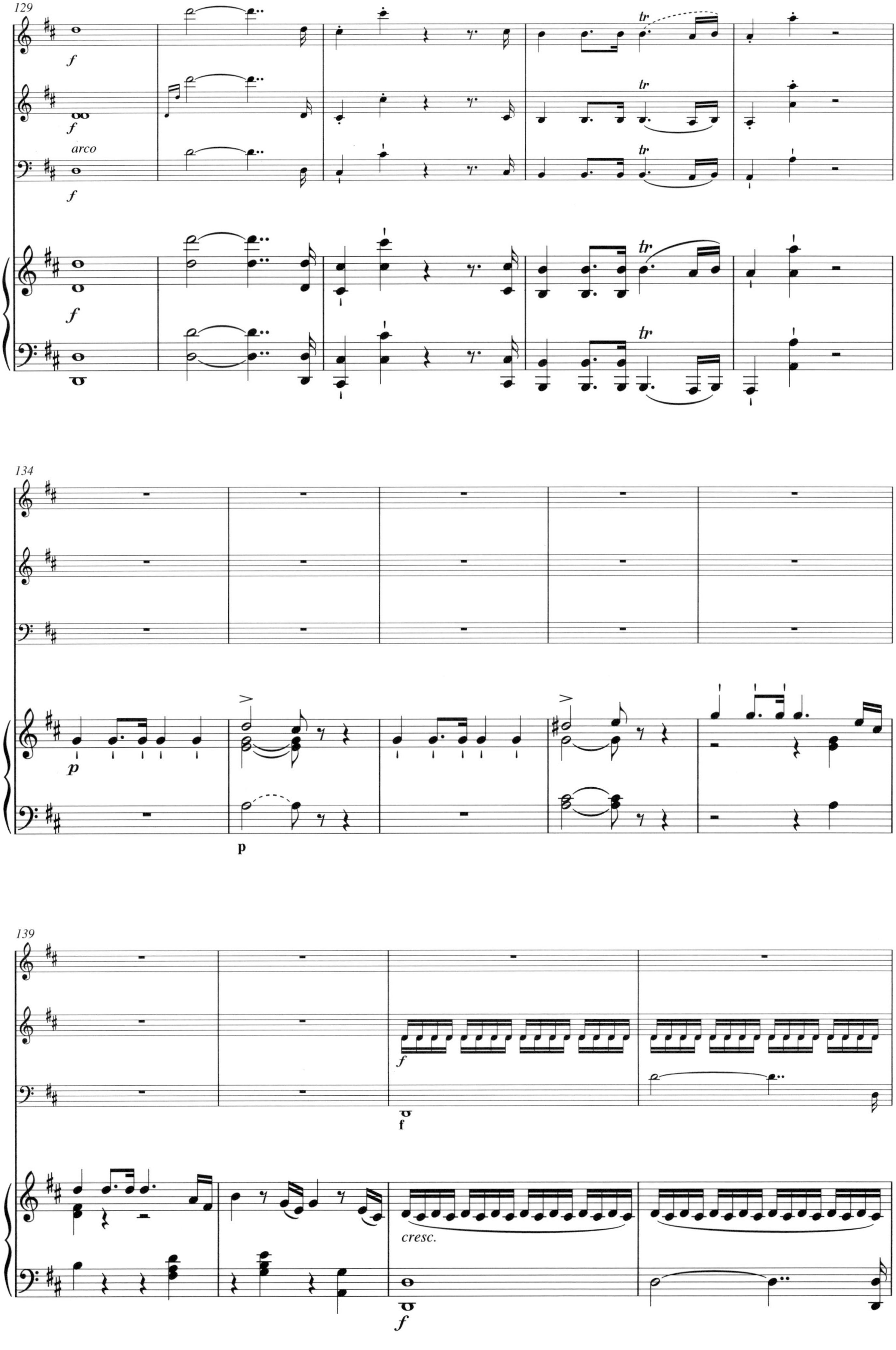
129
f
f
arco
f
tr
tr
tr
tr
f
134
p
p
139
f
f
cresc.
f

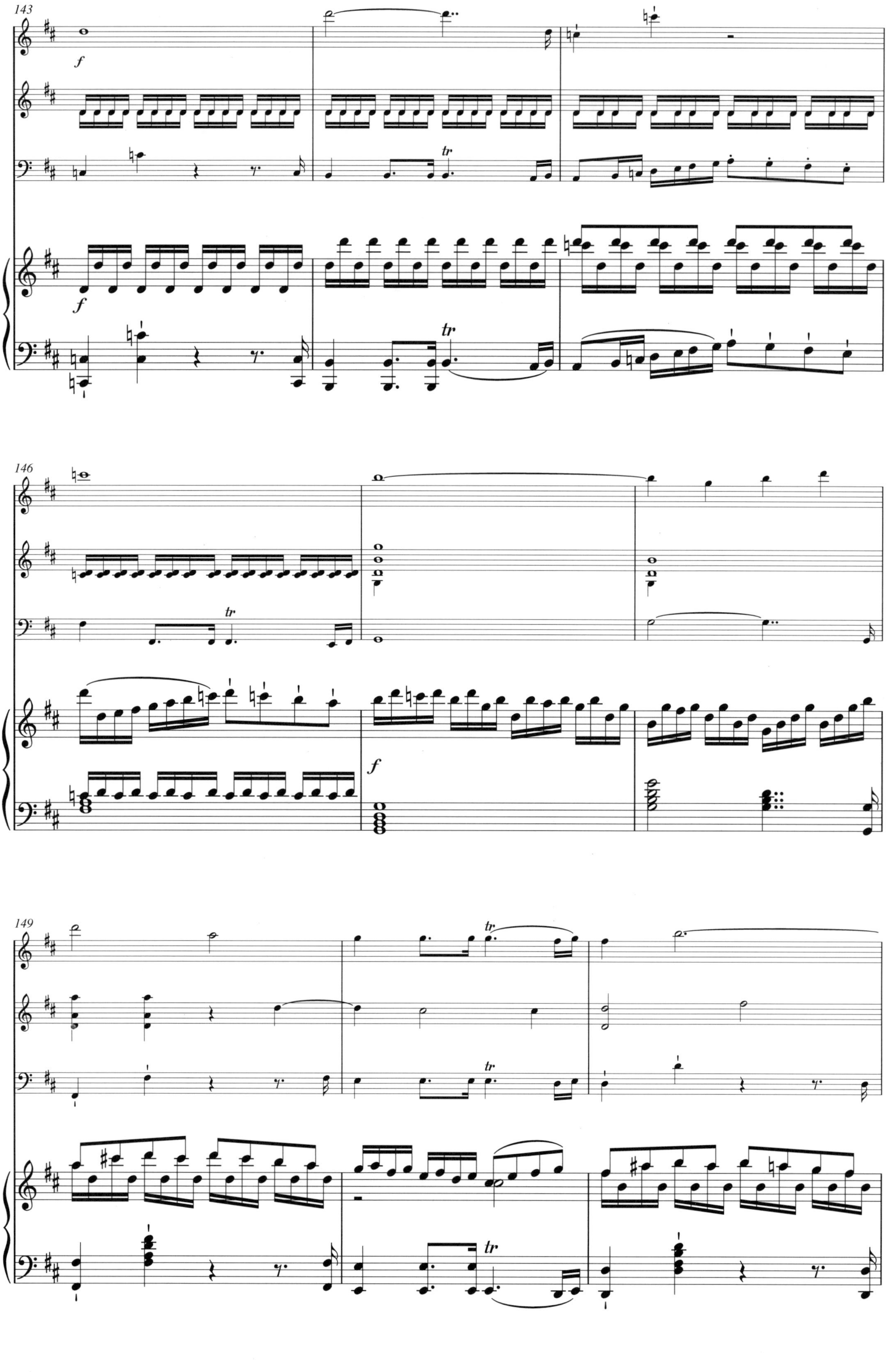
143
f
tr
f
tr
146
tr
f
149
tr
tr
tr

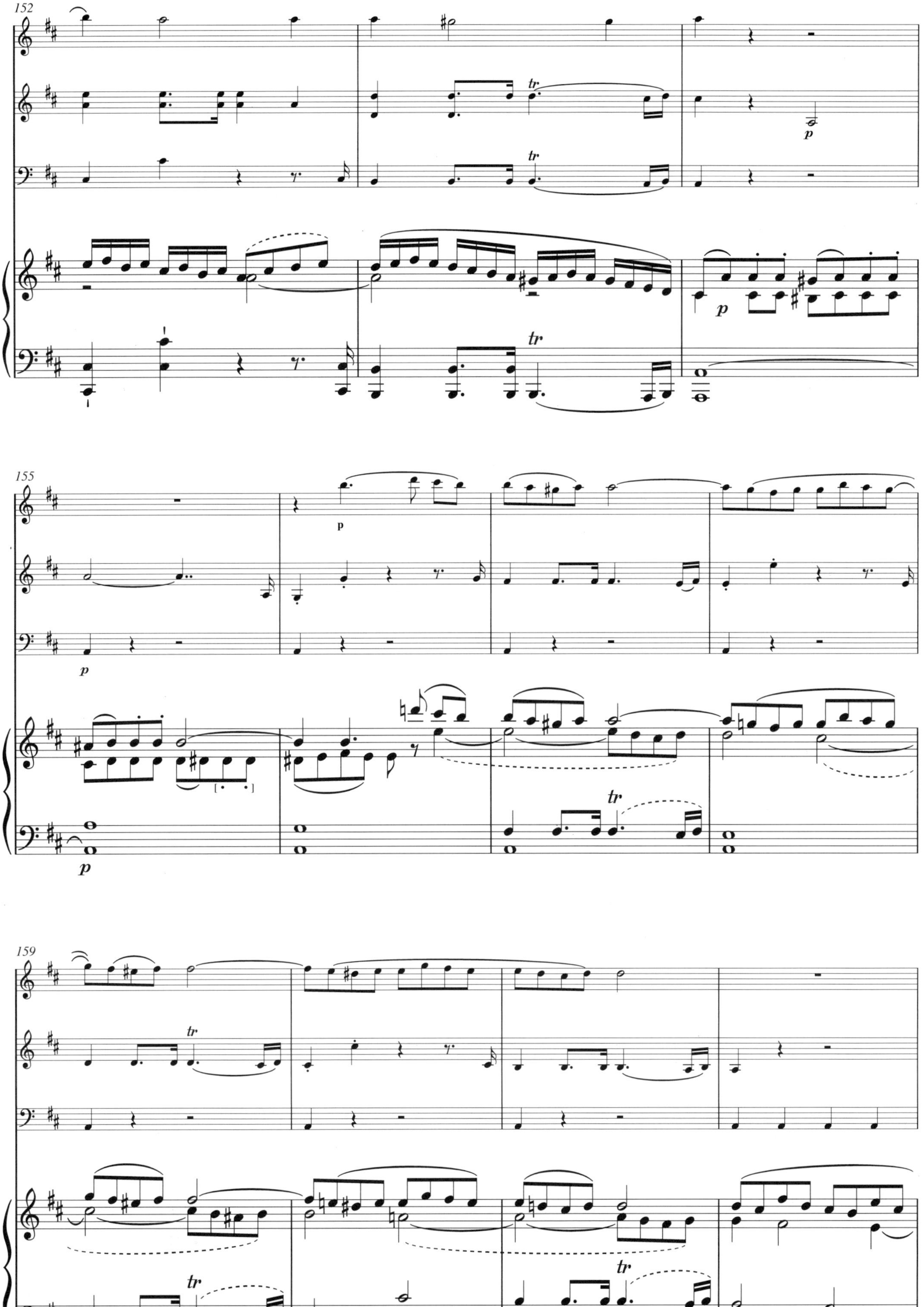
152
tr
p
tr
tr
155
p
p
p
tr
159
tr
tr
tr

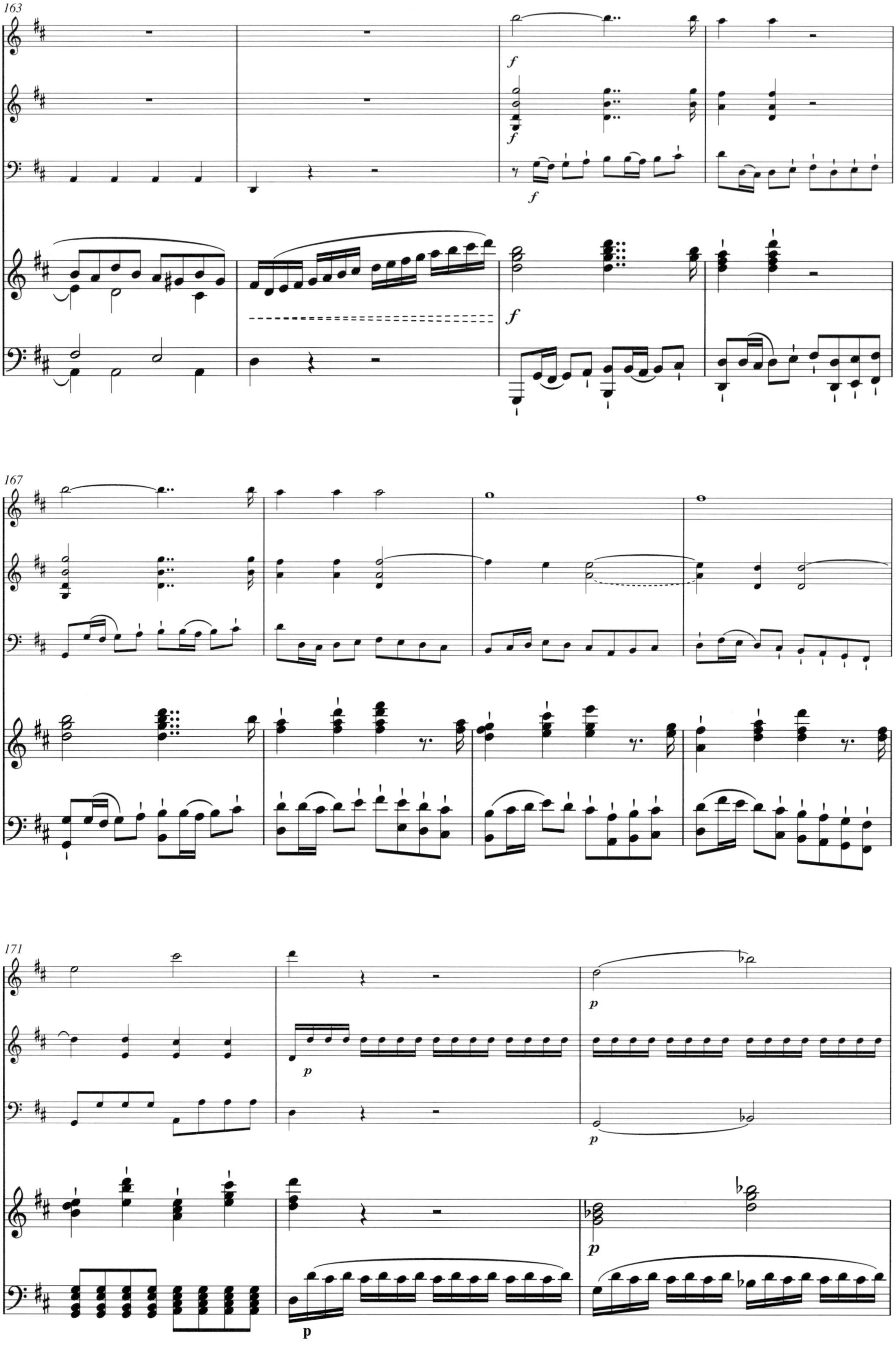
163
167
171

17

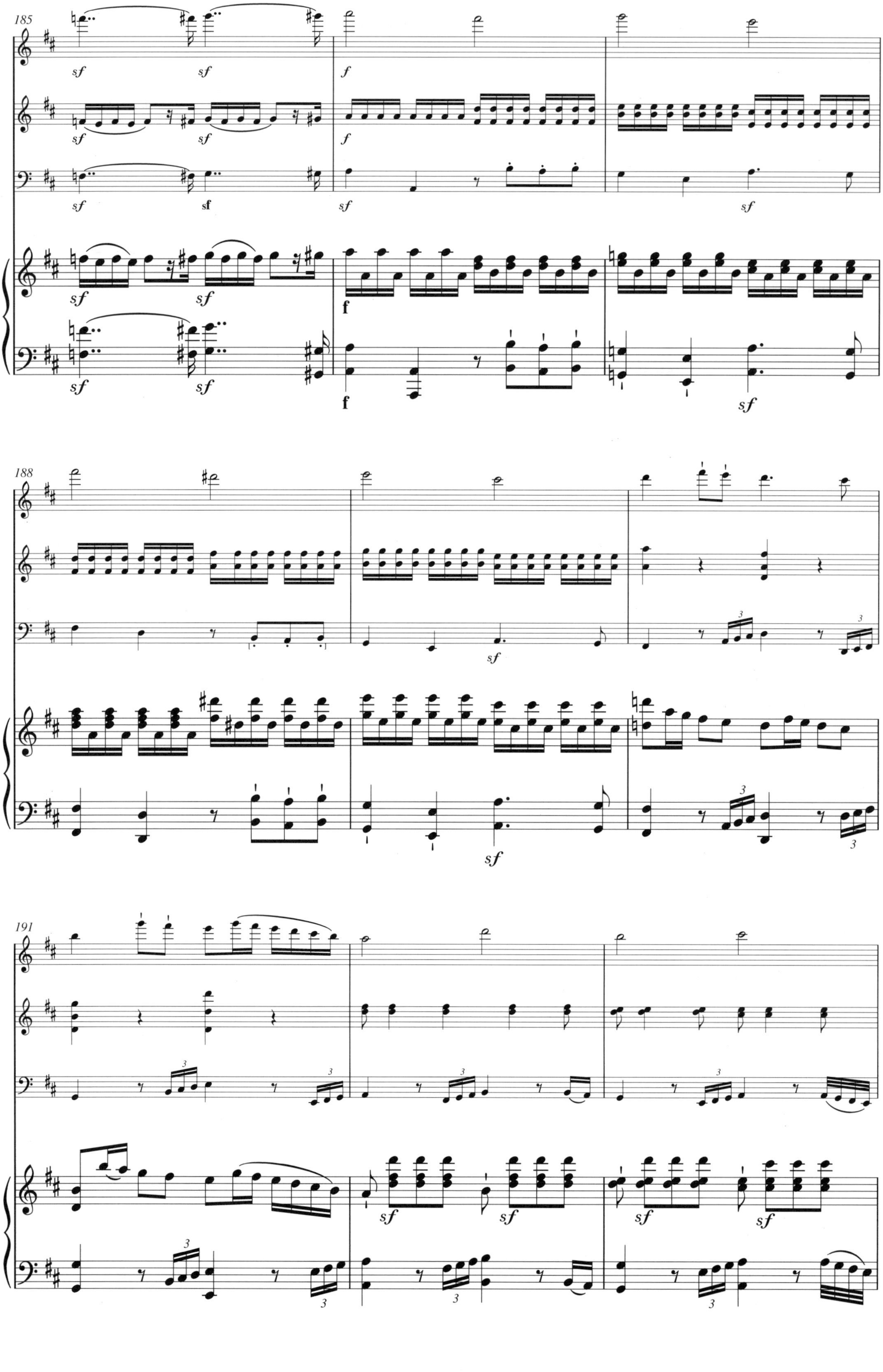
185
188
191

19

II

21

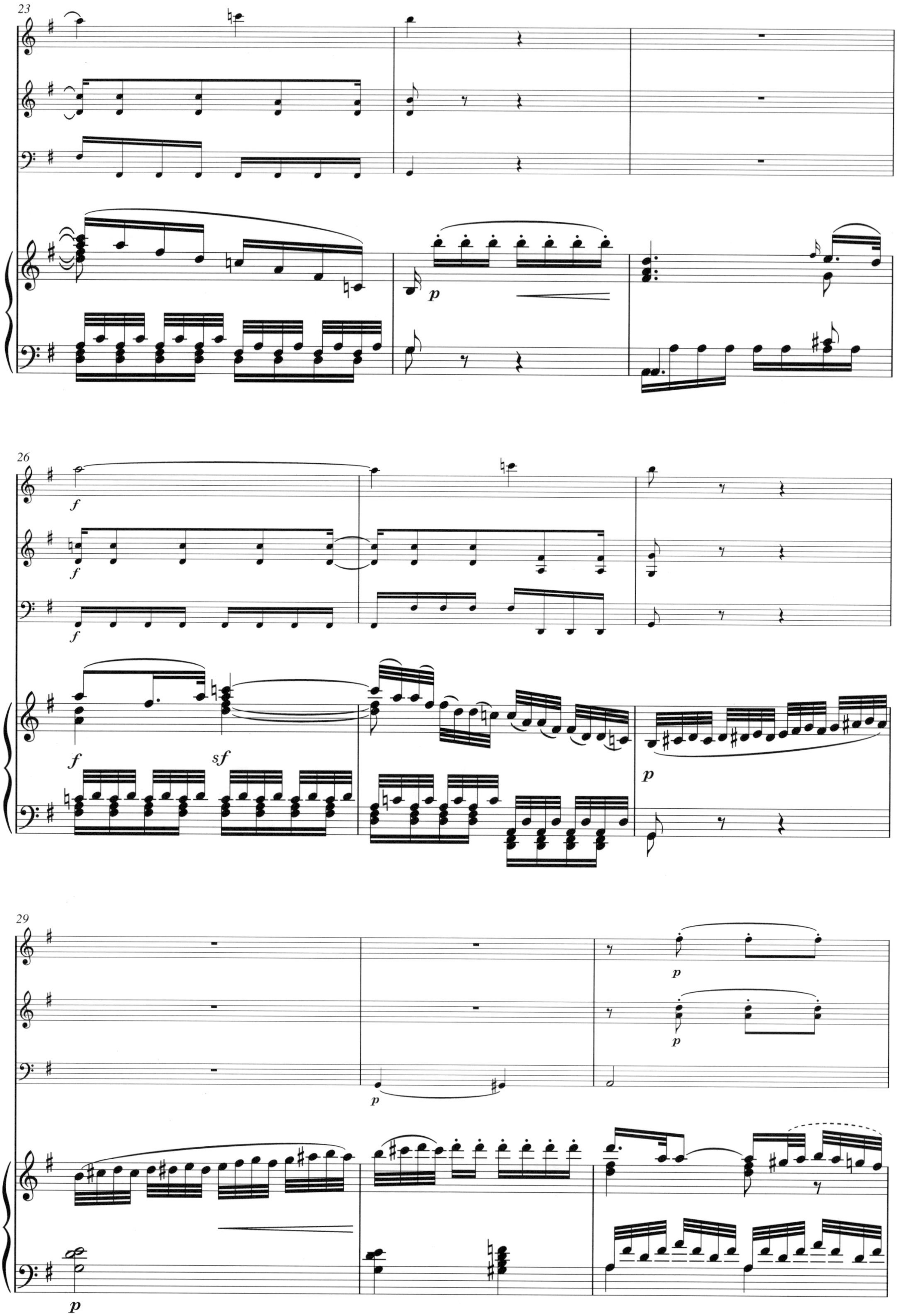
23
26
29

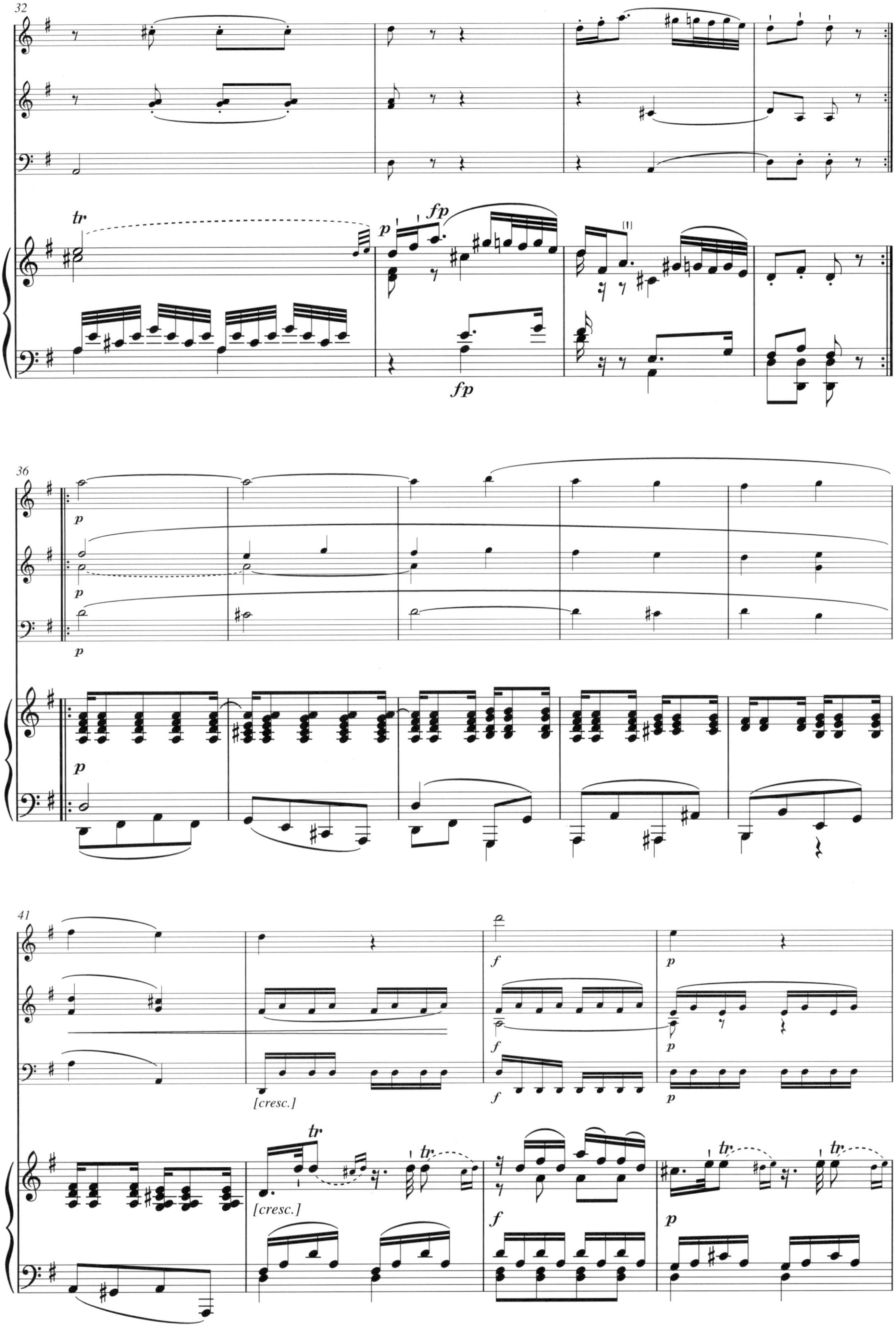
32
tr
p
fp
fp
[!]
36
p
p
p
p
41
[cresc.]
[cresc.]
tr
f
f
f
p
p
p

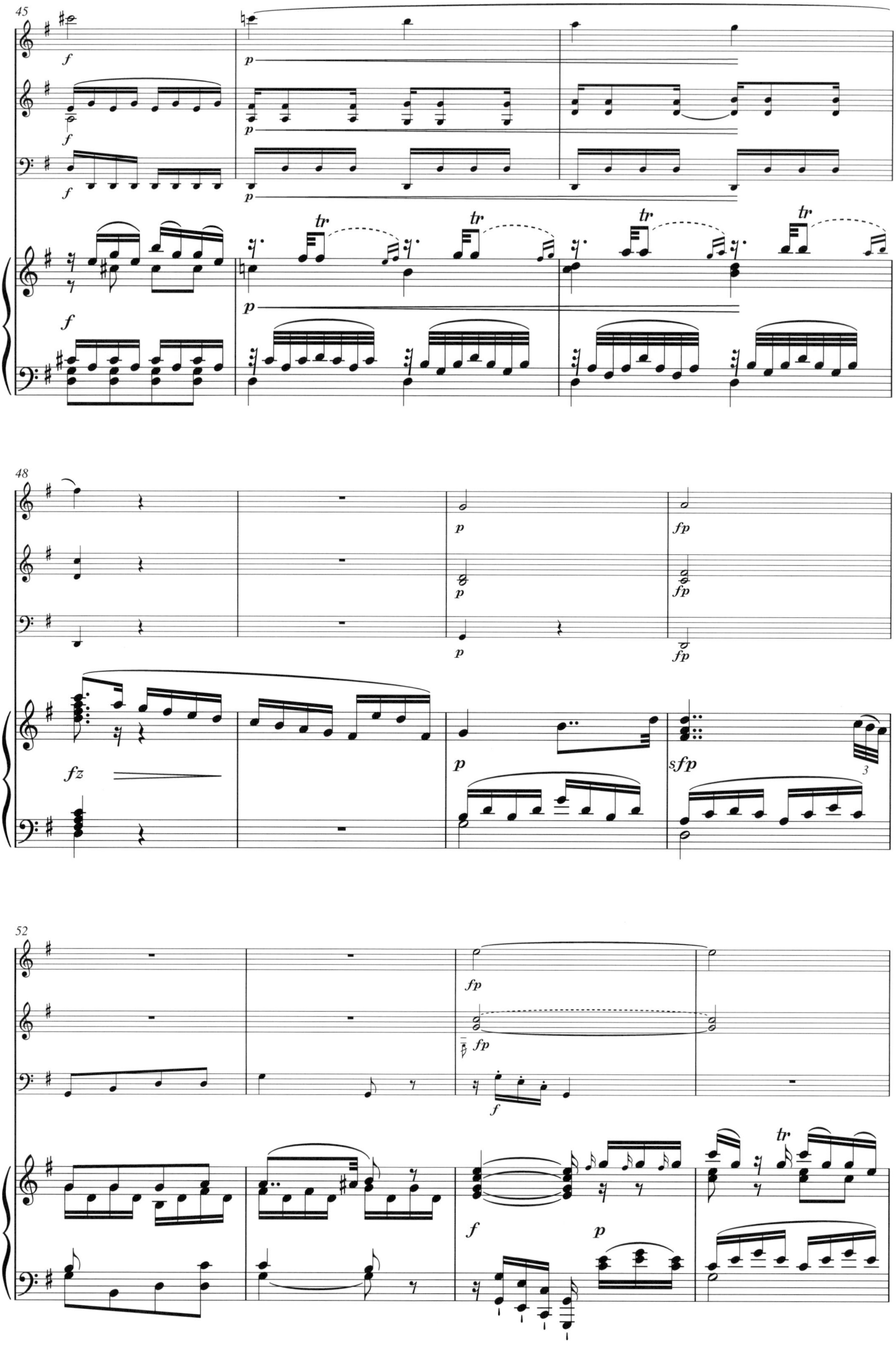

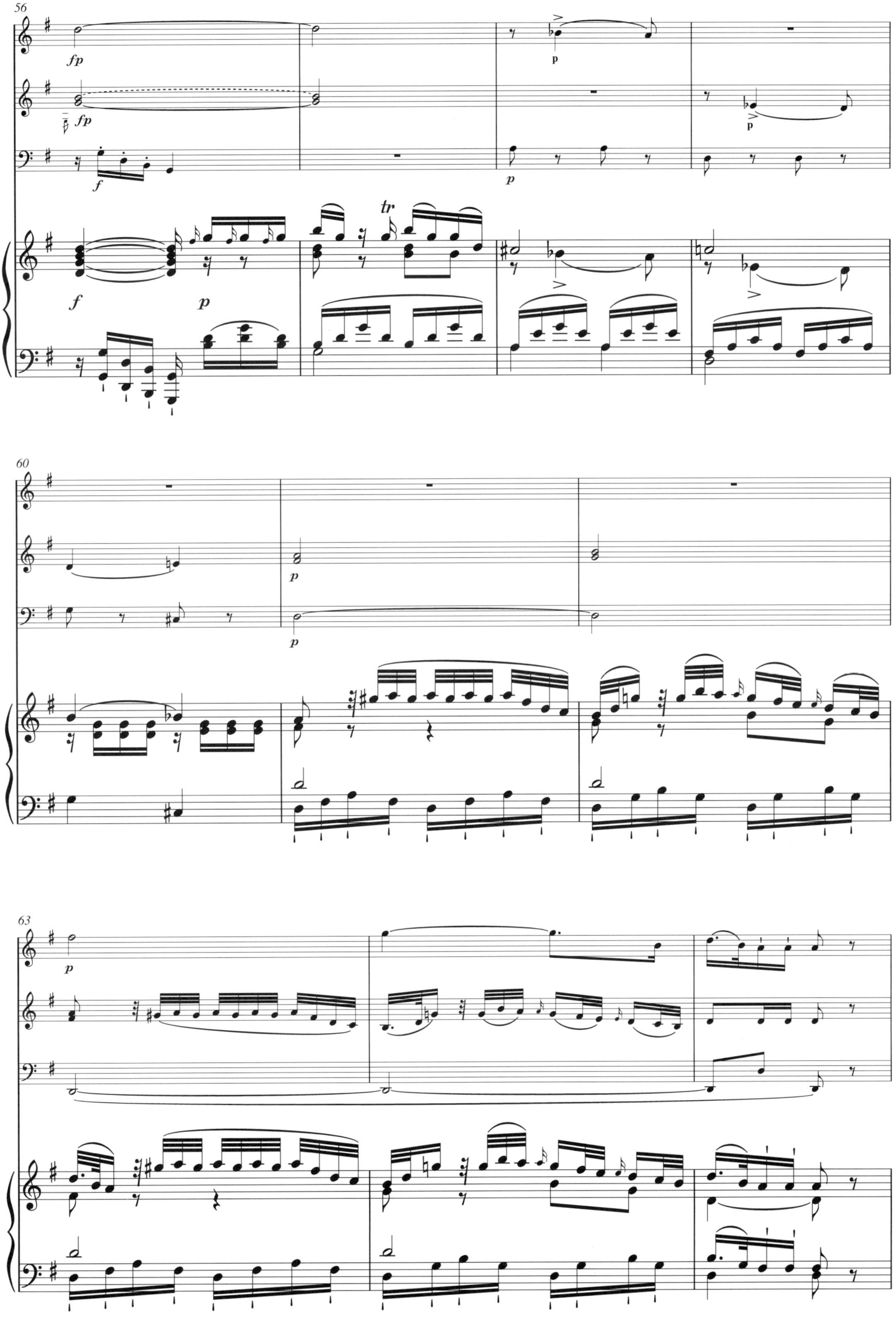
56
fp
p
fp
f
f
p
tr
p
60
p
p
63
p

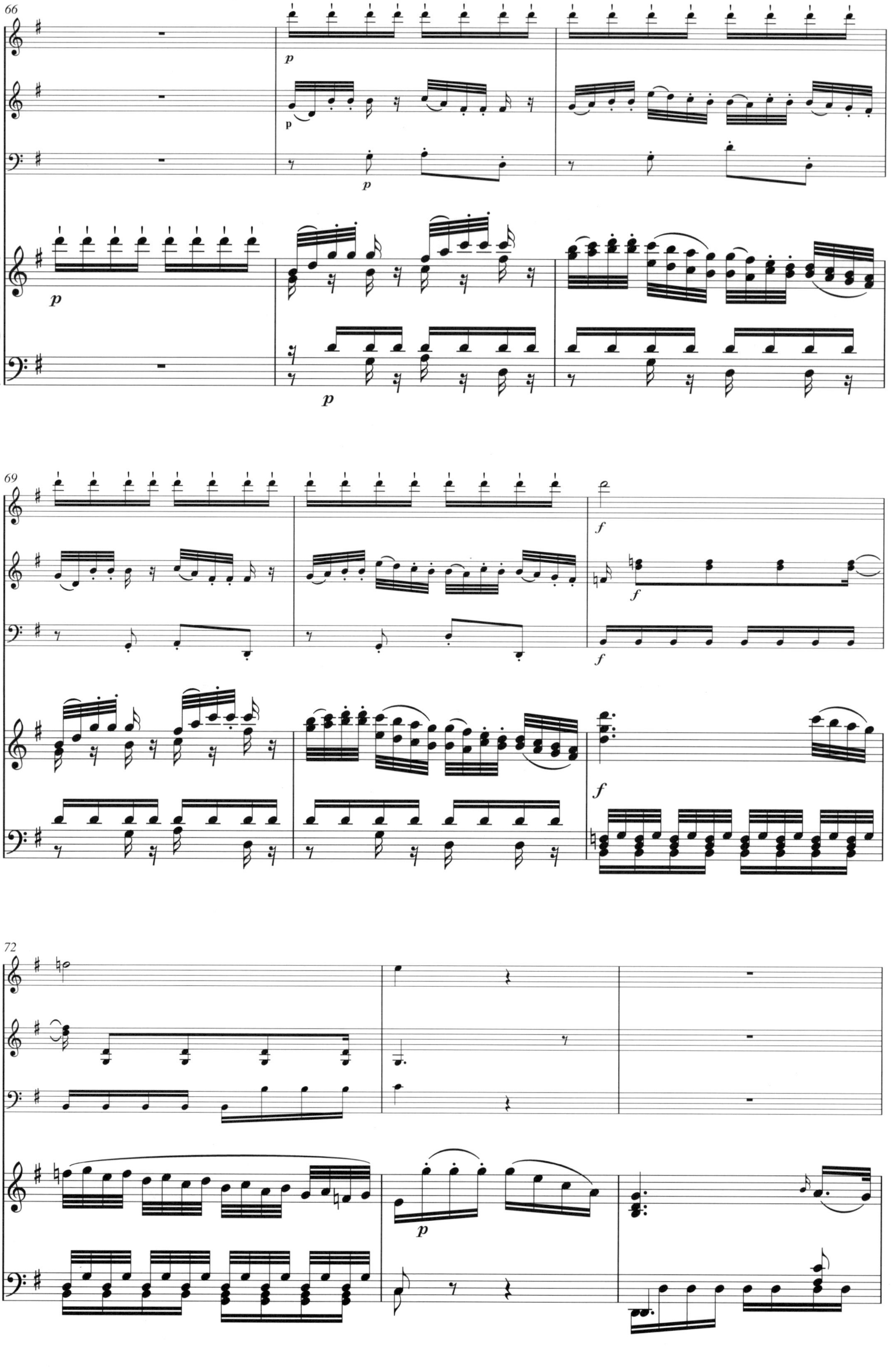
66
69
72

27

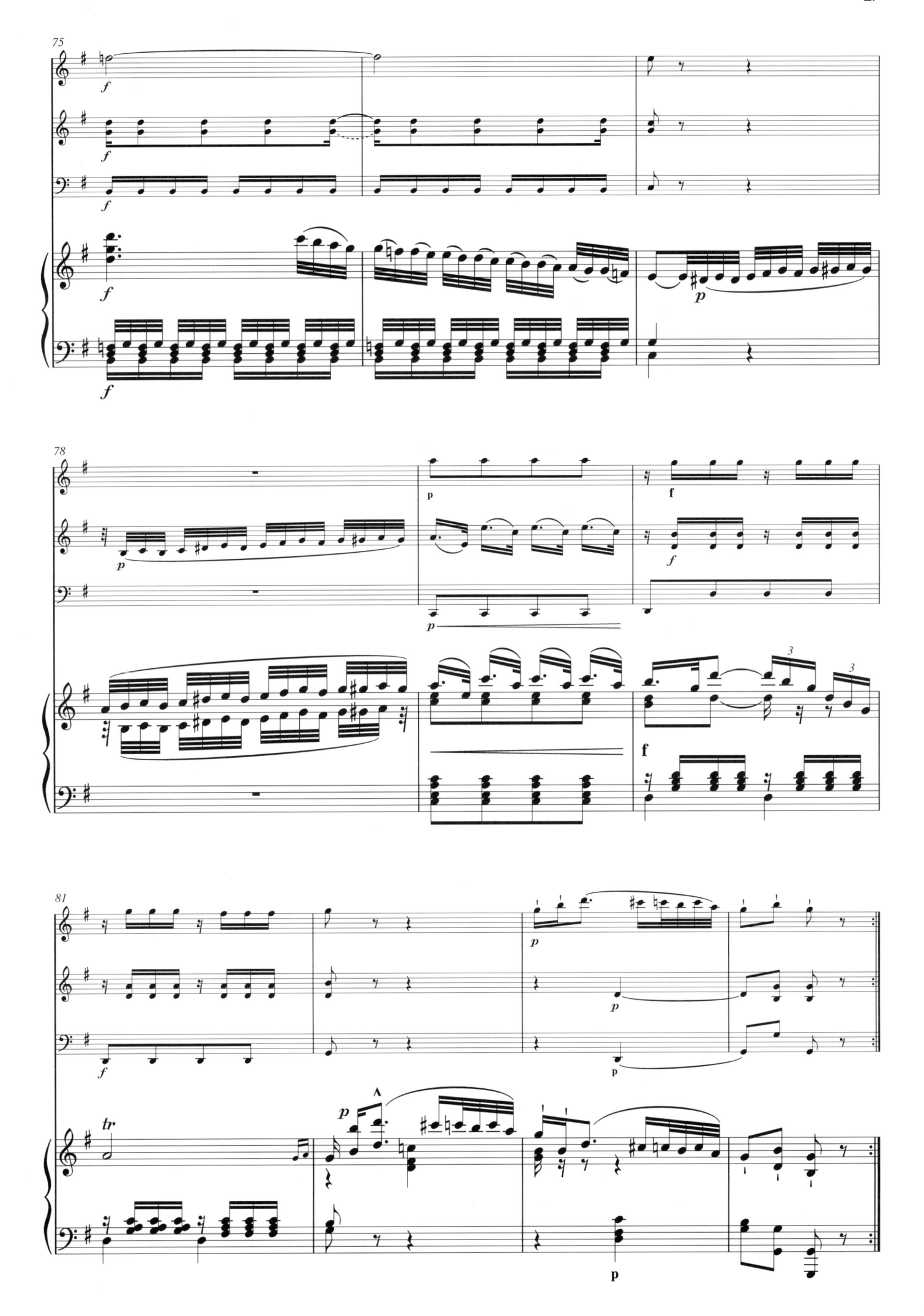

III

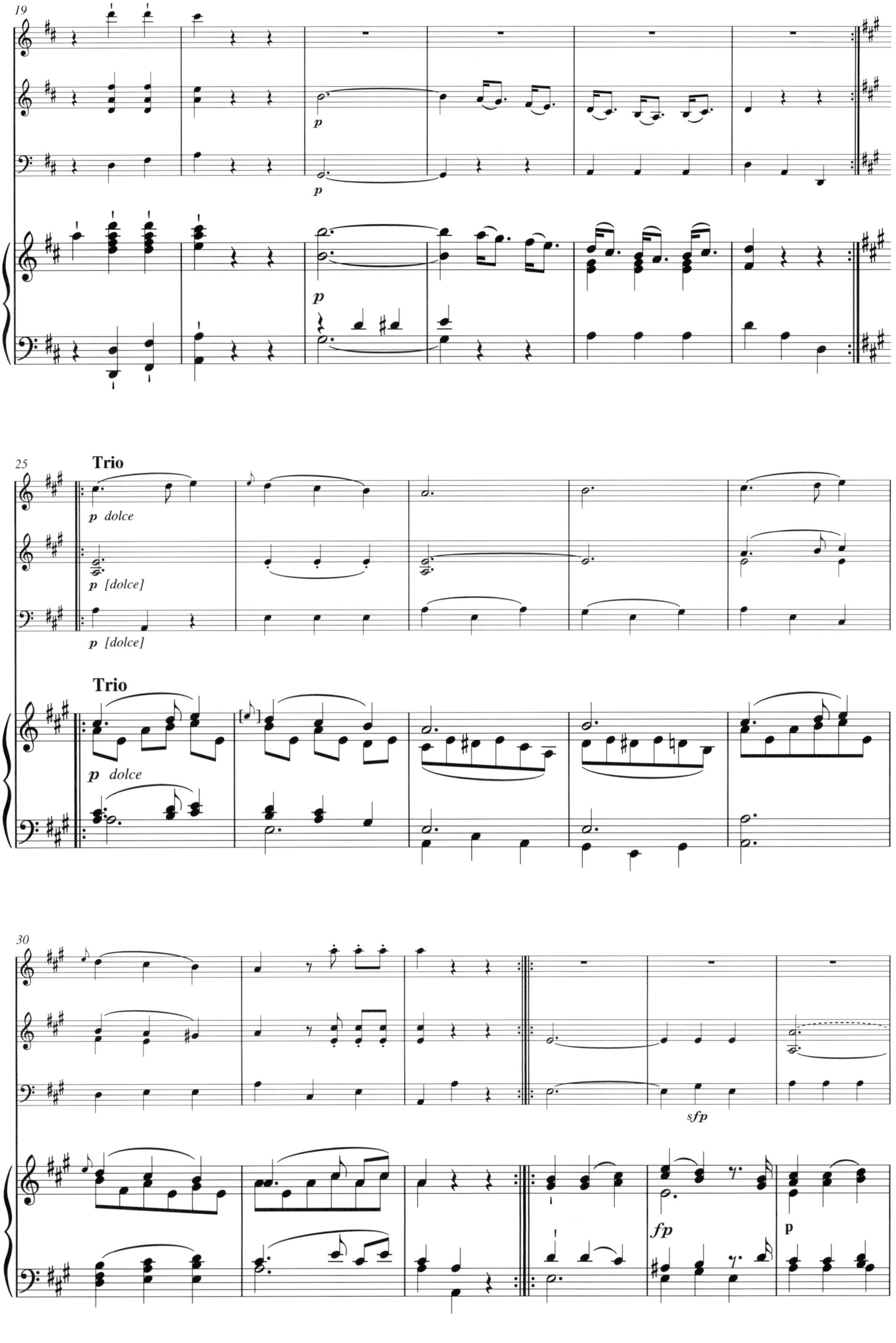
19
p
p
p
25
Trio
p dolce
p [dolce]
p [dolce]
Trio
p dolce
30
sfp
fp
p

Min[uetto] da capo

[Minuetto da capo]

IV

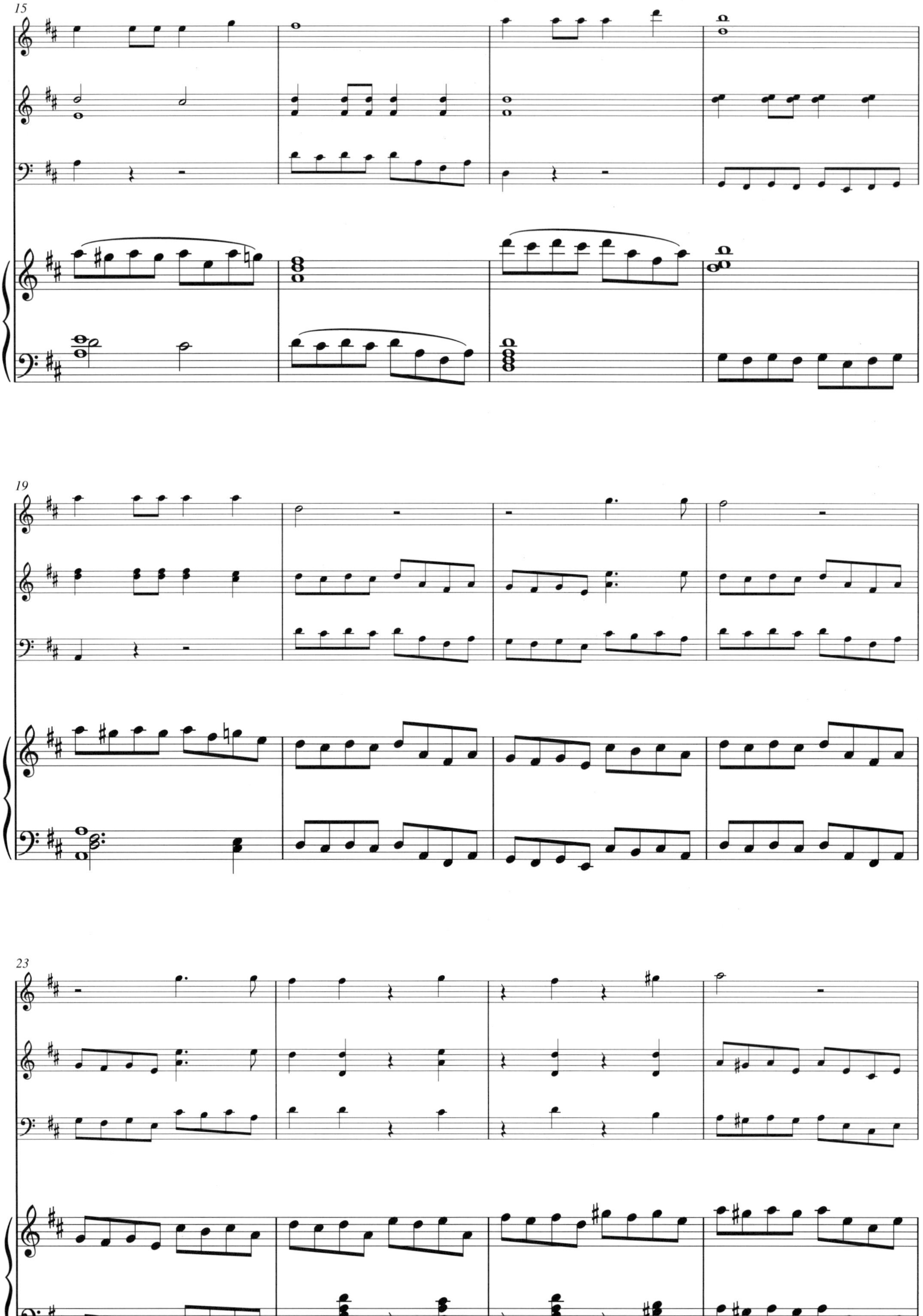
15
19
23

33

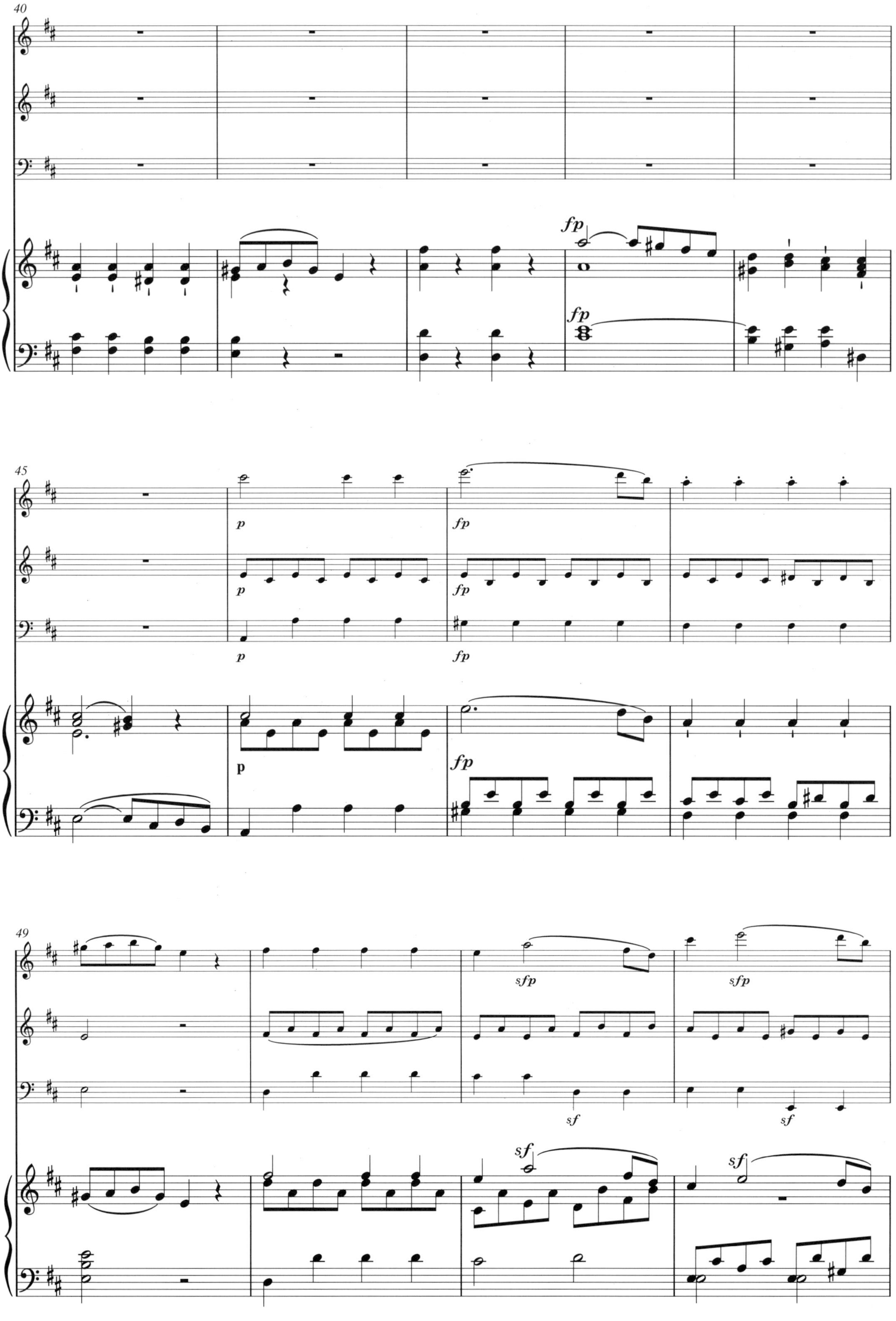
40
fp
fp
45
p
fp
p
fp
p
fp
p
fp
49
sfp
sfp
sf
sf
sf
sf

35

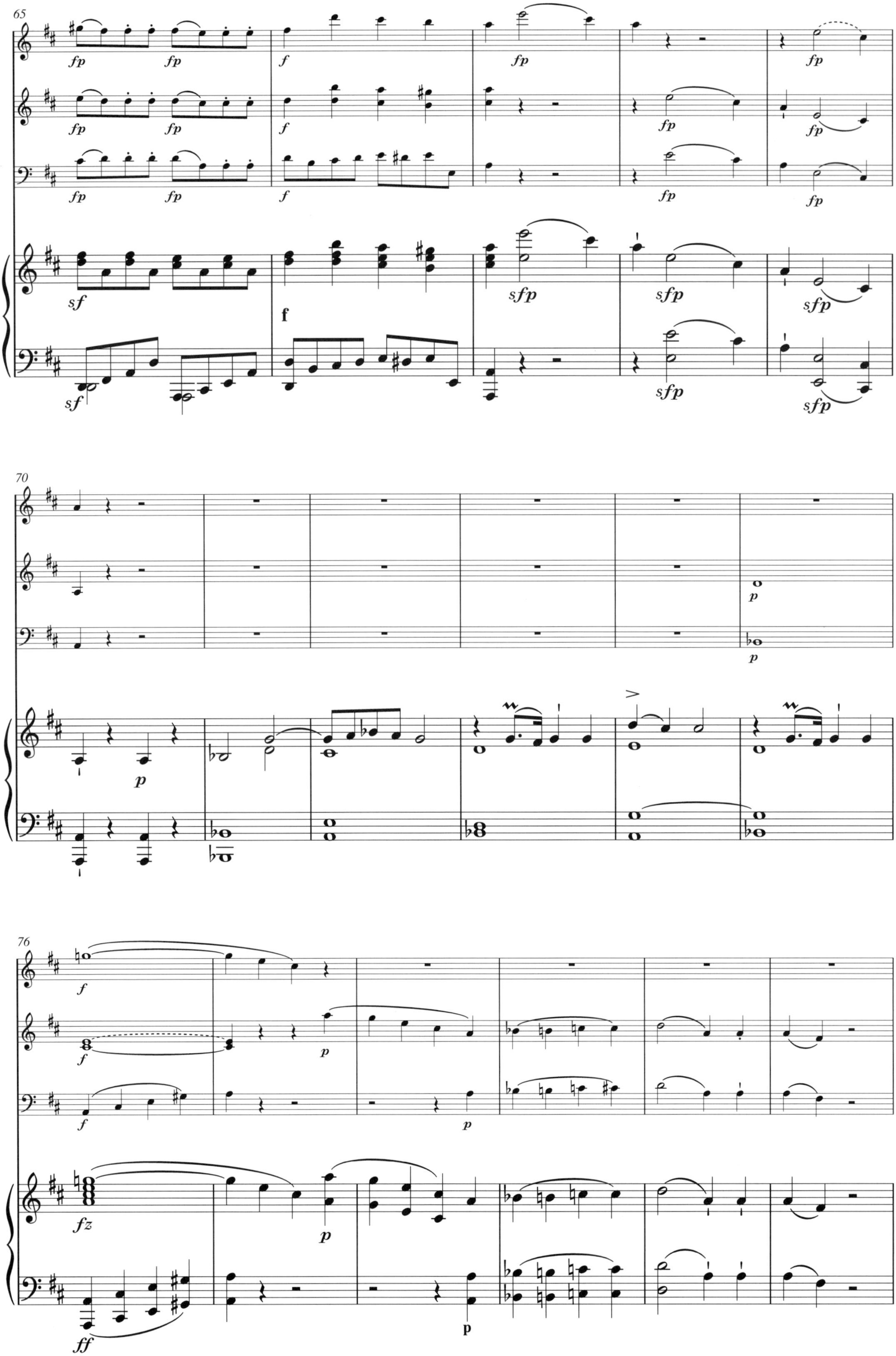

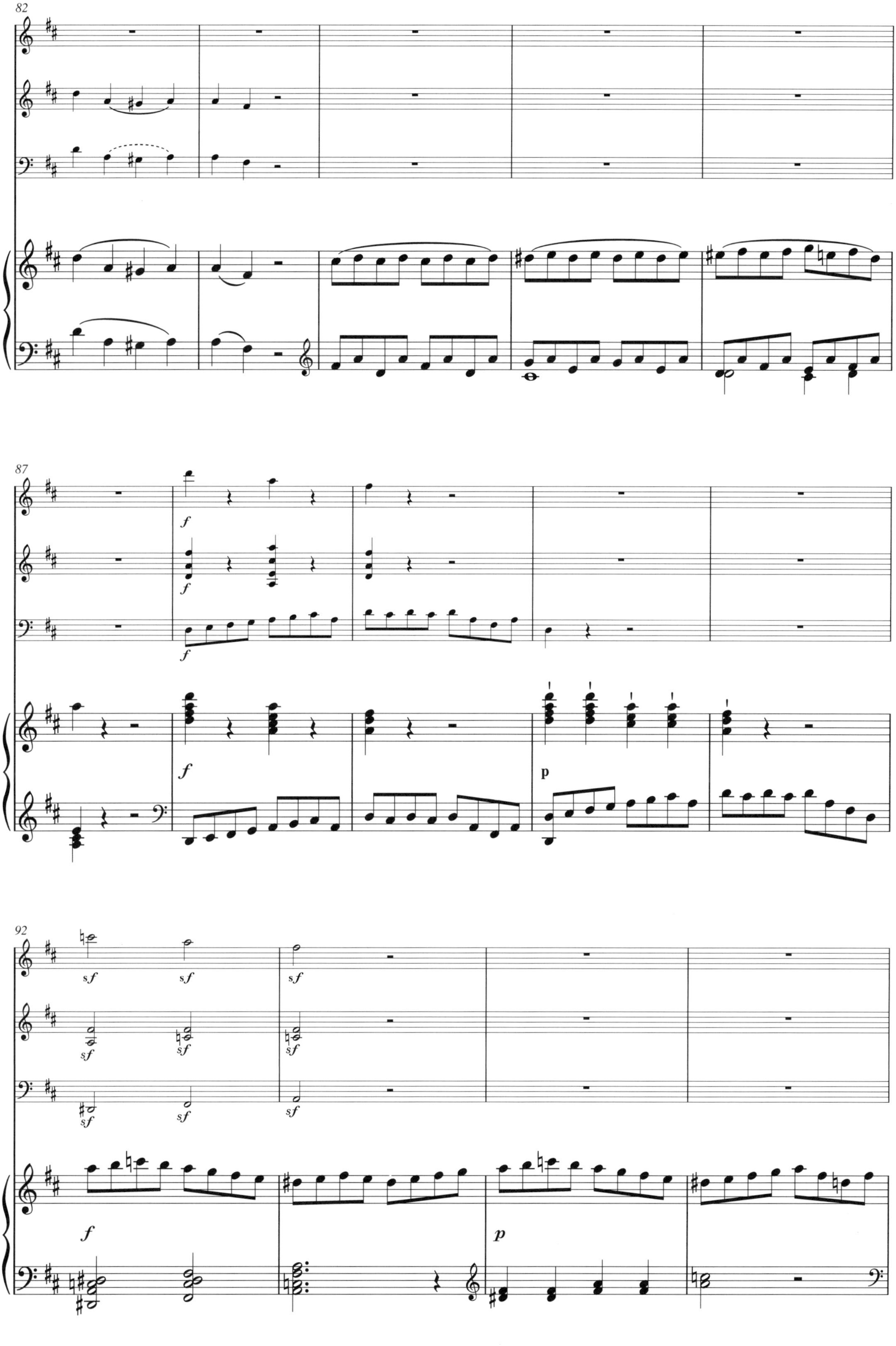
82
87
f
f
f
f
p
92
sf
sf
sf
sf
sf
sf
sf
sf
sf
f
p

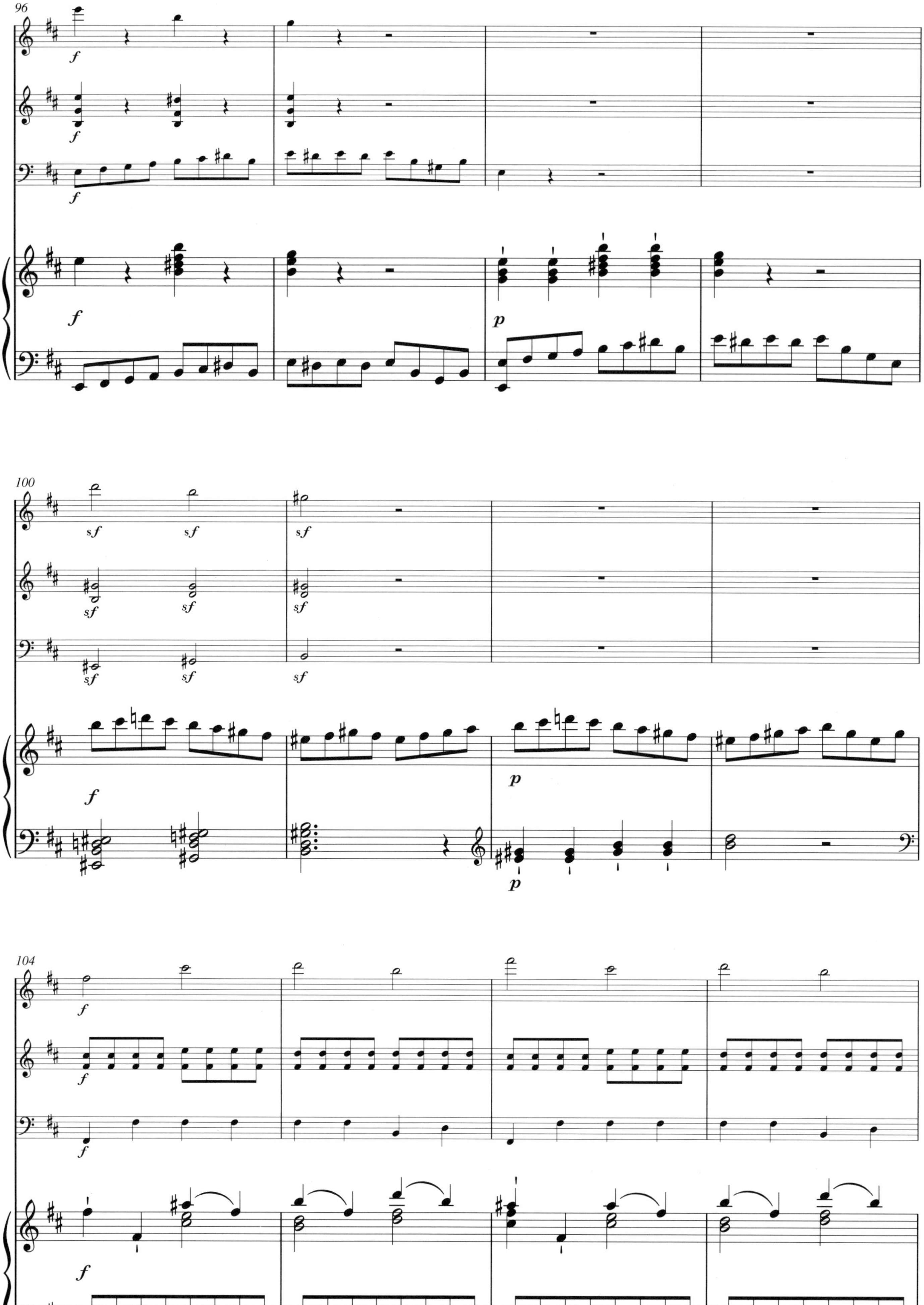
96
100
104

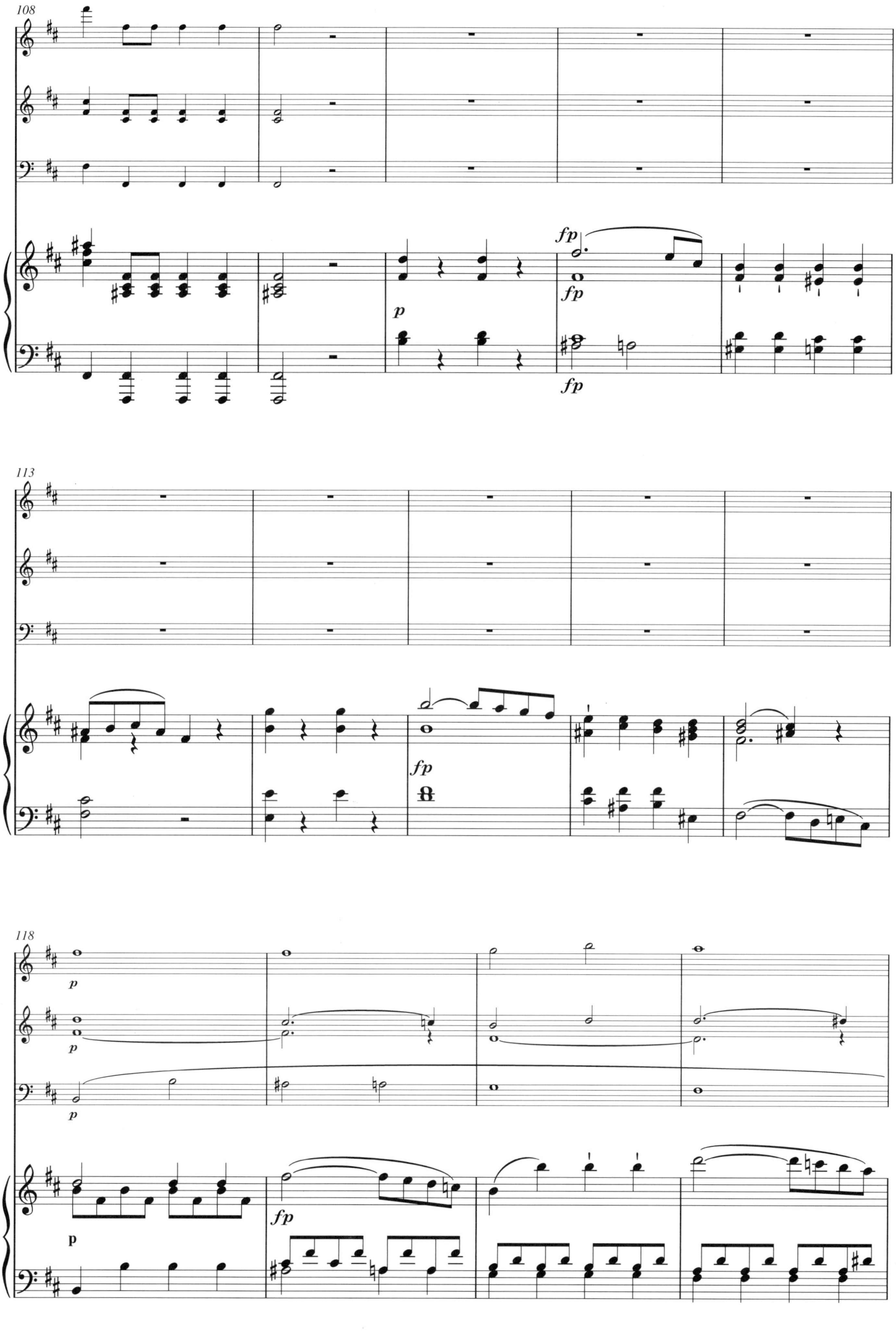
108
113
118

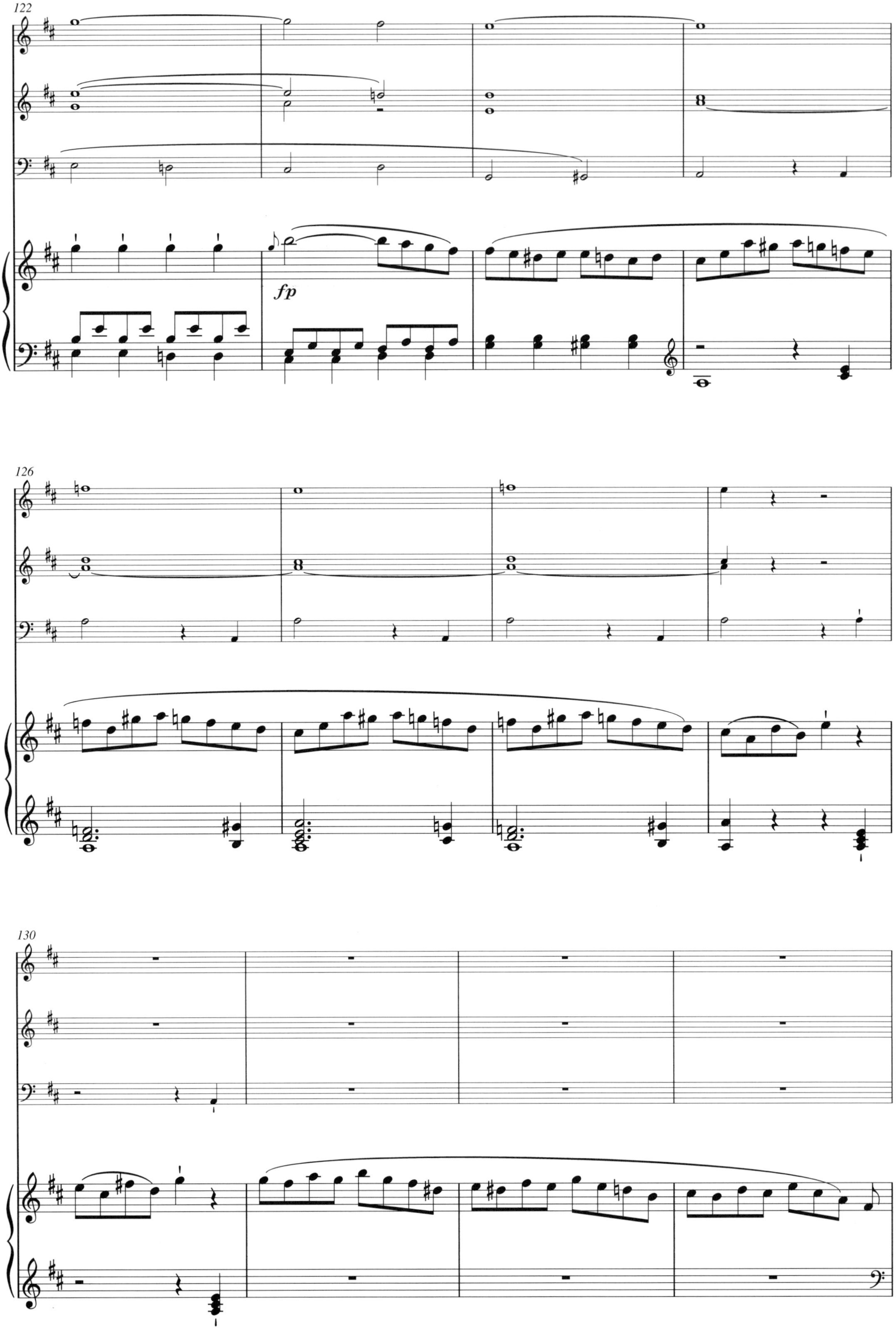
122
fp
126
130

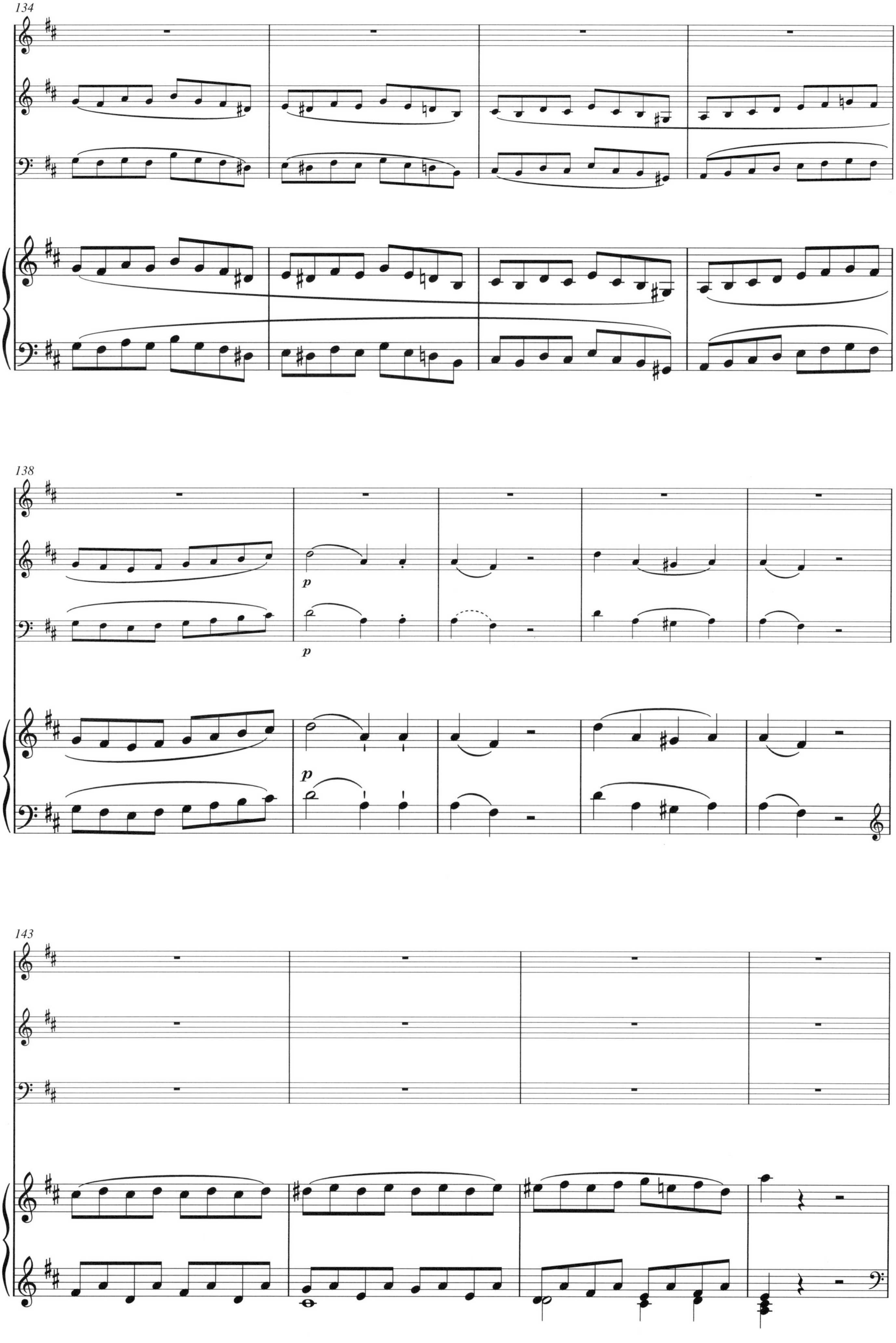
134
138
p
p
p
143

42

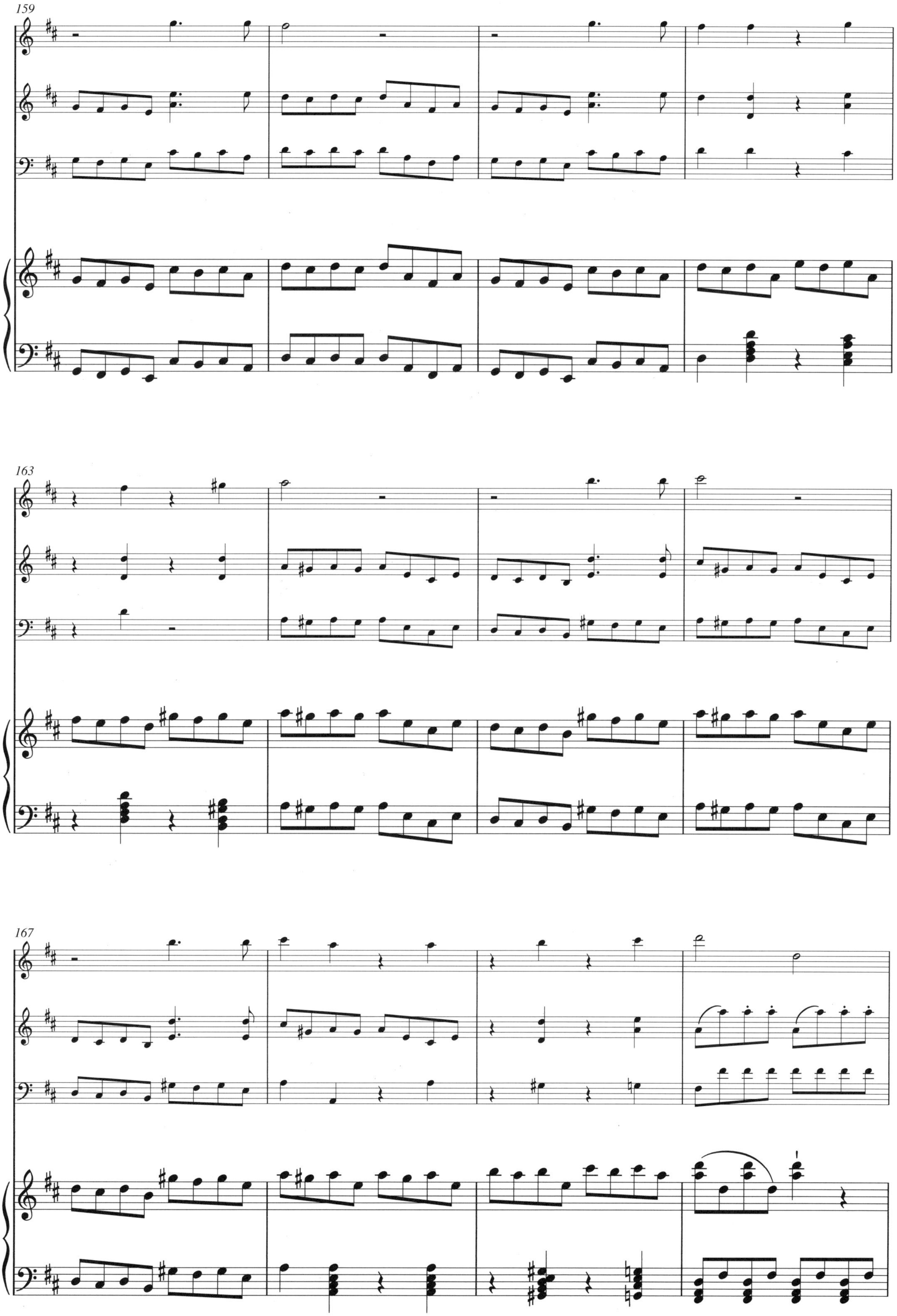
159
163
167

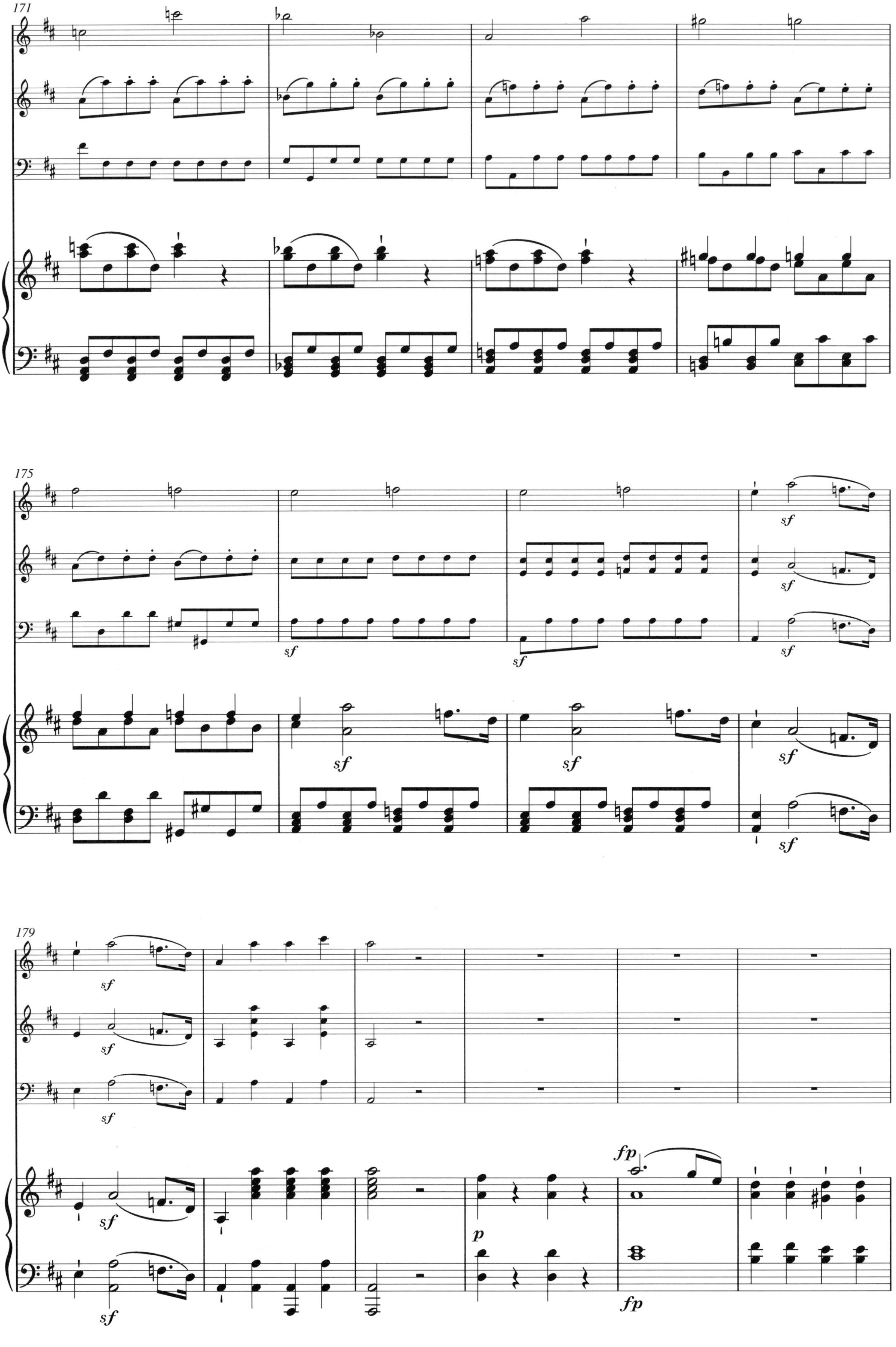
171
175
sf
sf
sf
sf
179
sf
p
fp
fp

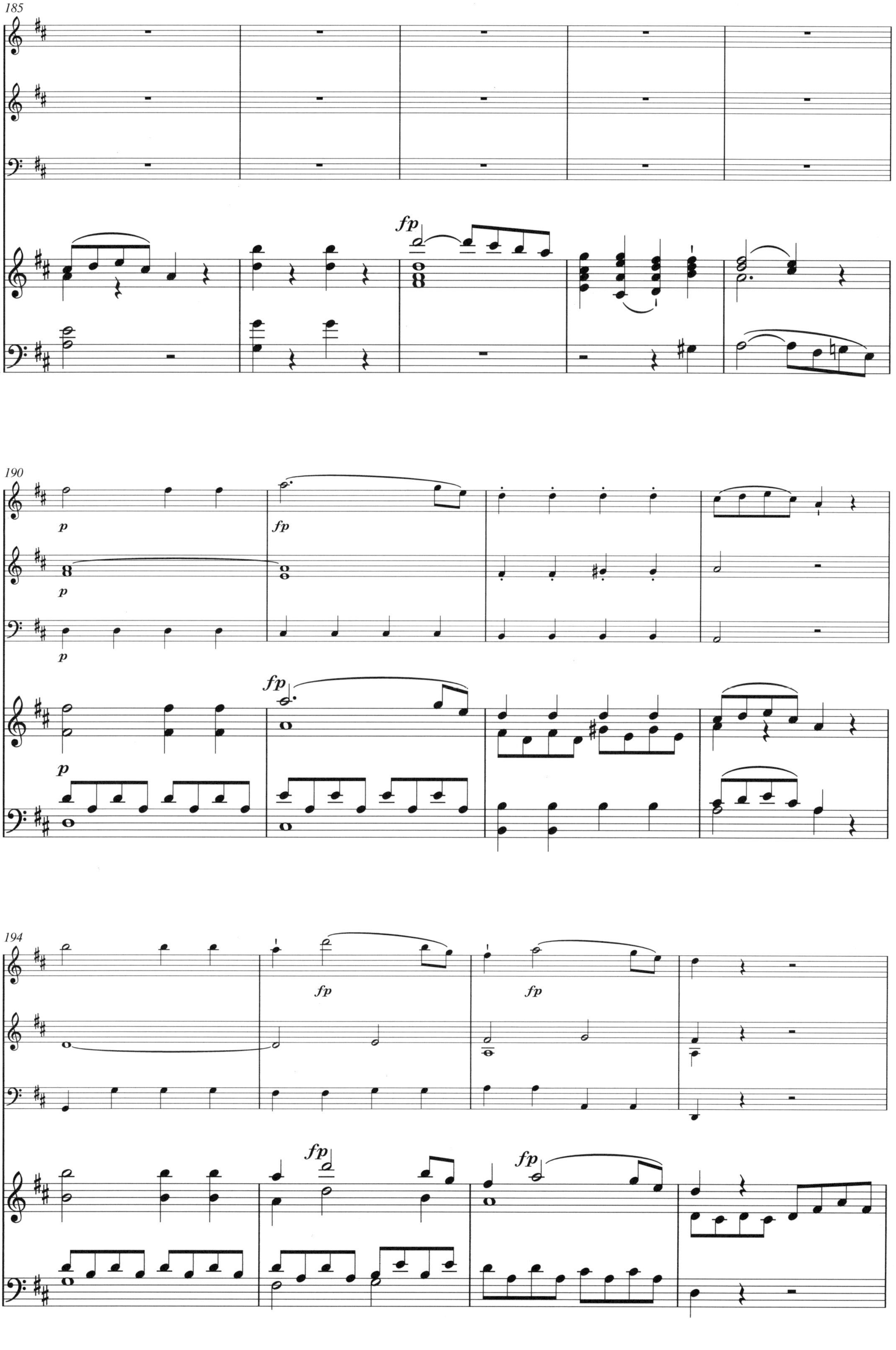
185
fp
190
p
fp
p
p
fp
p
194
fp
fp
fp
fp

46

47

48

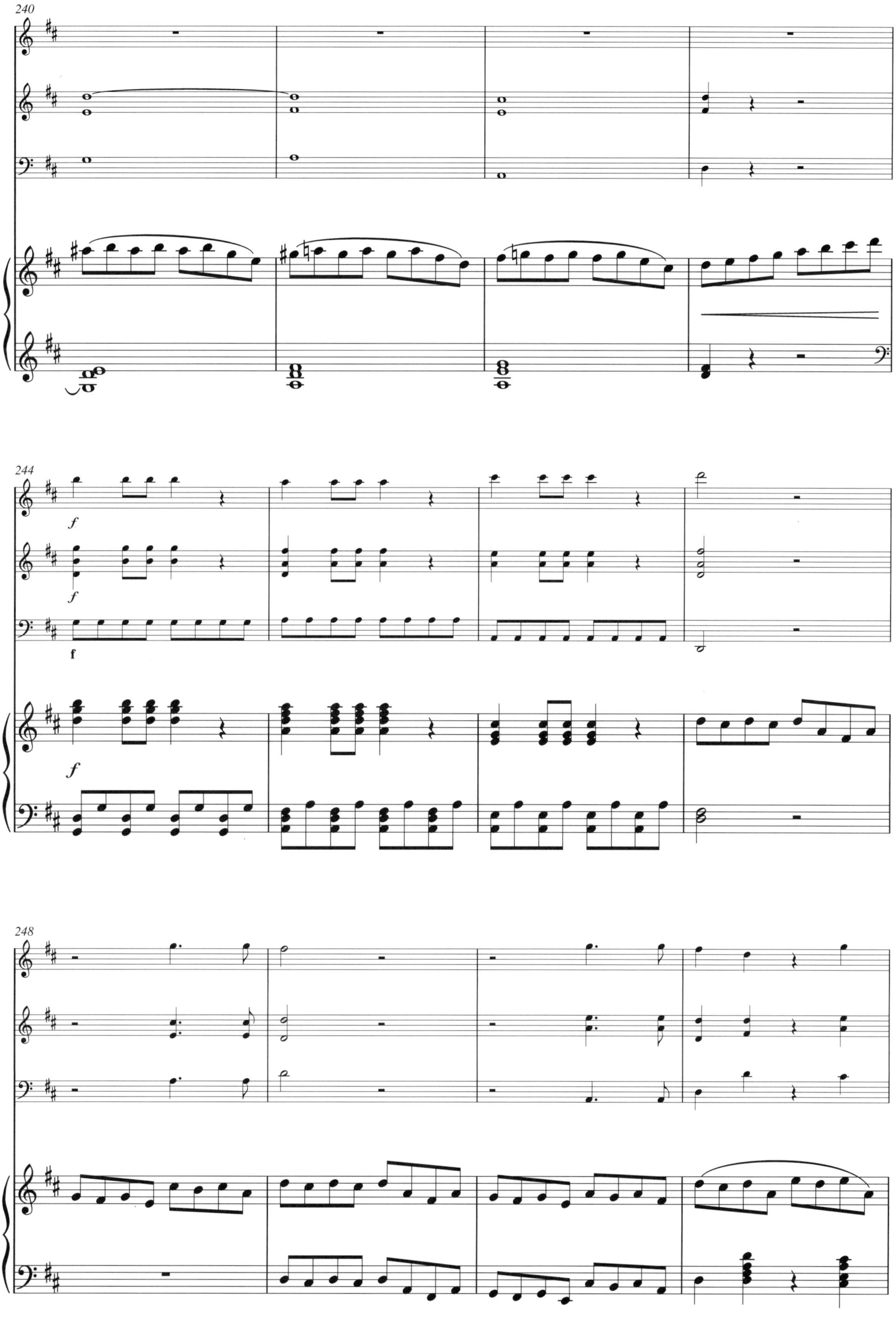
240
244
f
f
f
f
248

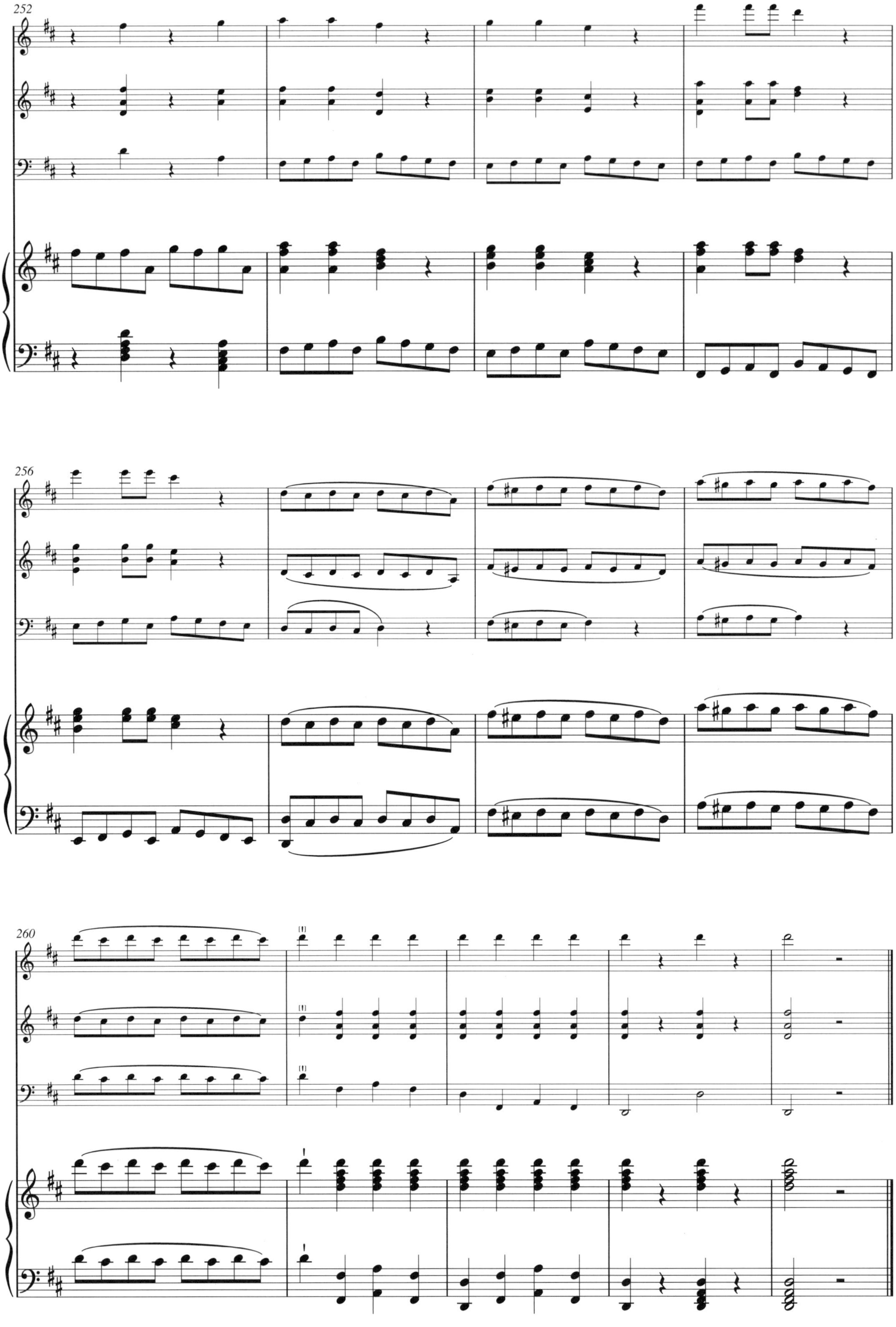
252
256
260

Symphony in C Major, K. 425 *(Linz)*
I

Wolfgang Amadeus Mozart

52

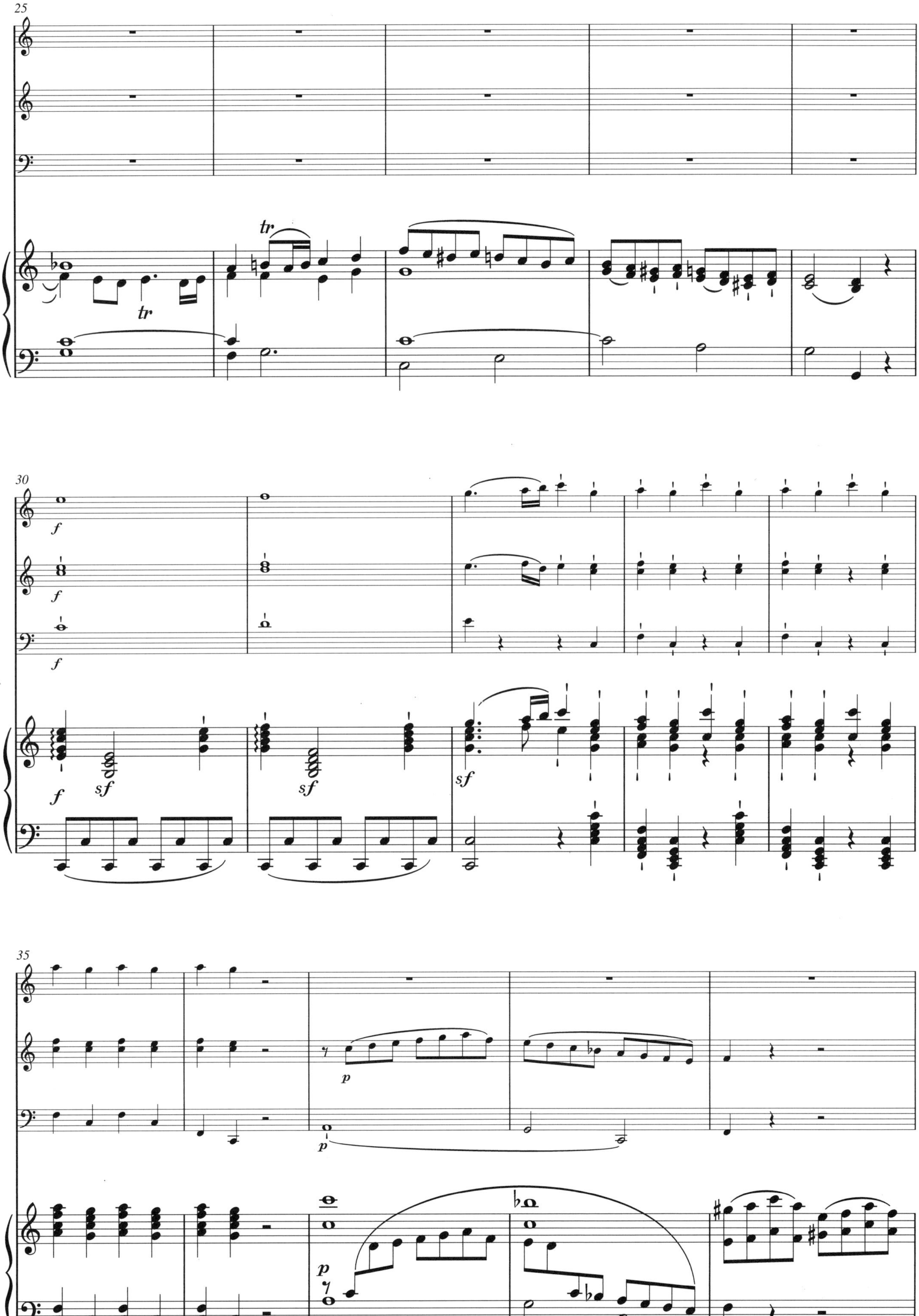
25
tr
tr
30
f
f
f
f
sf
sf
sf
35
p
p
p

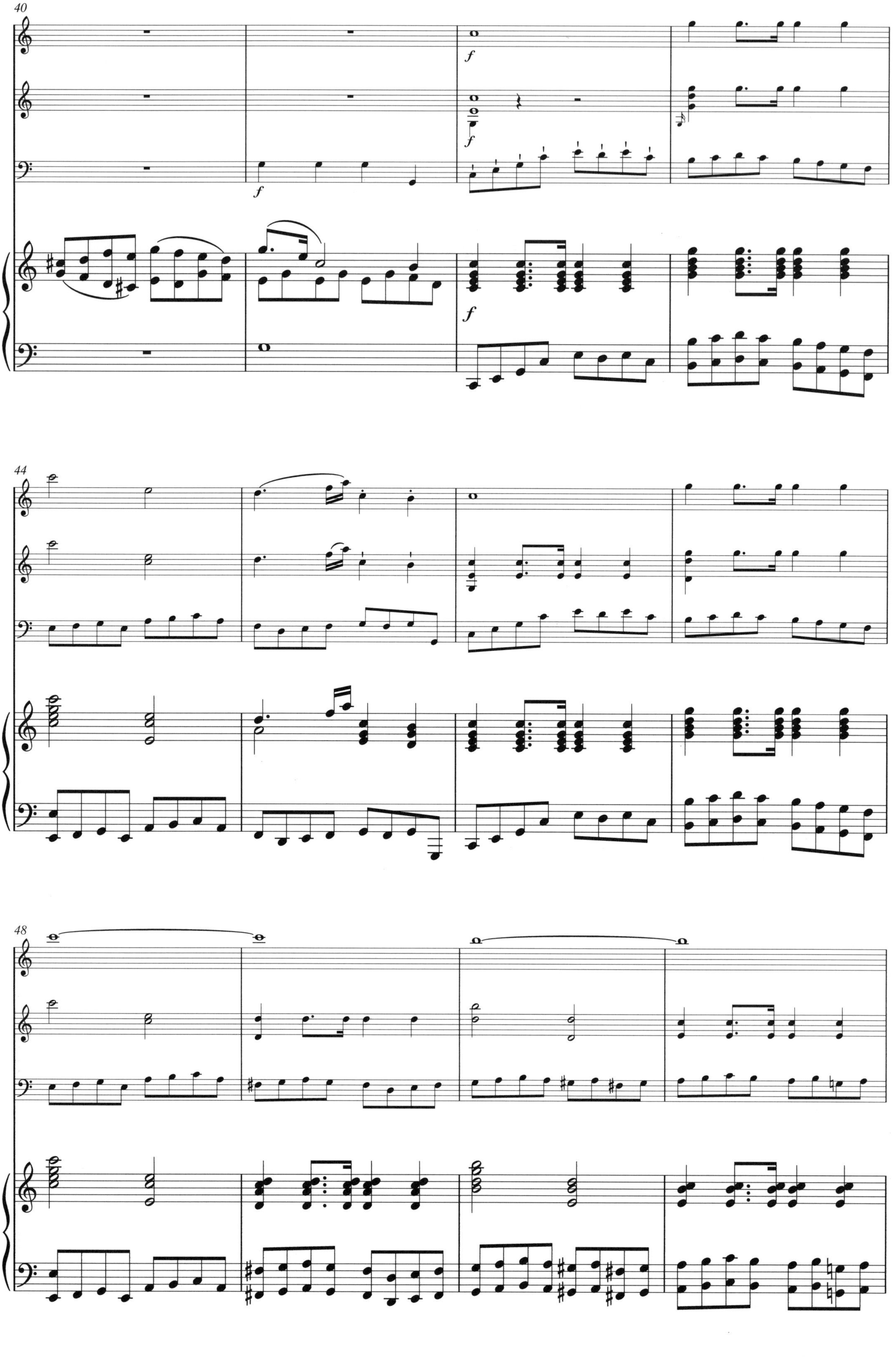
40
f
f
f
f
44
48

55

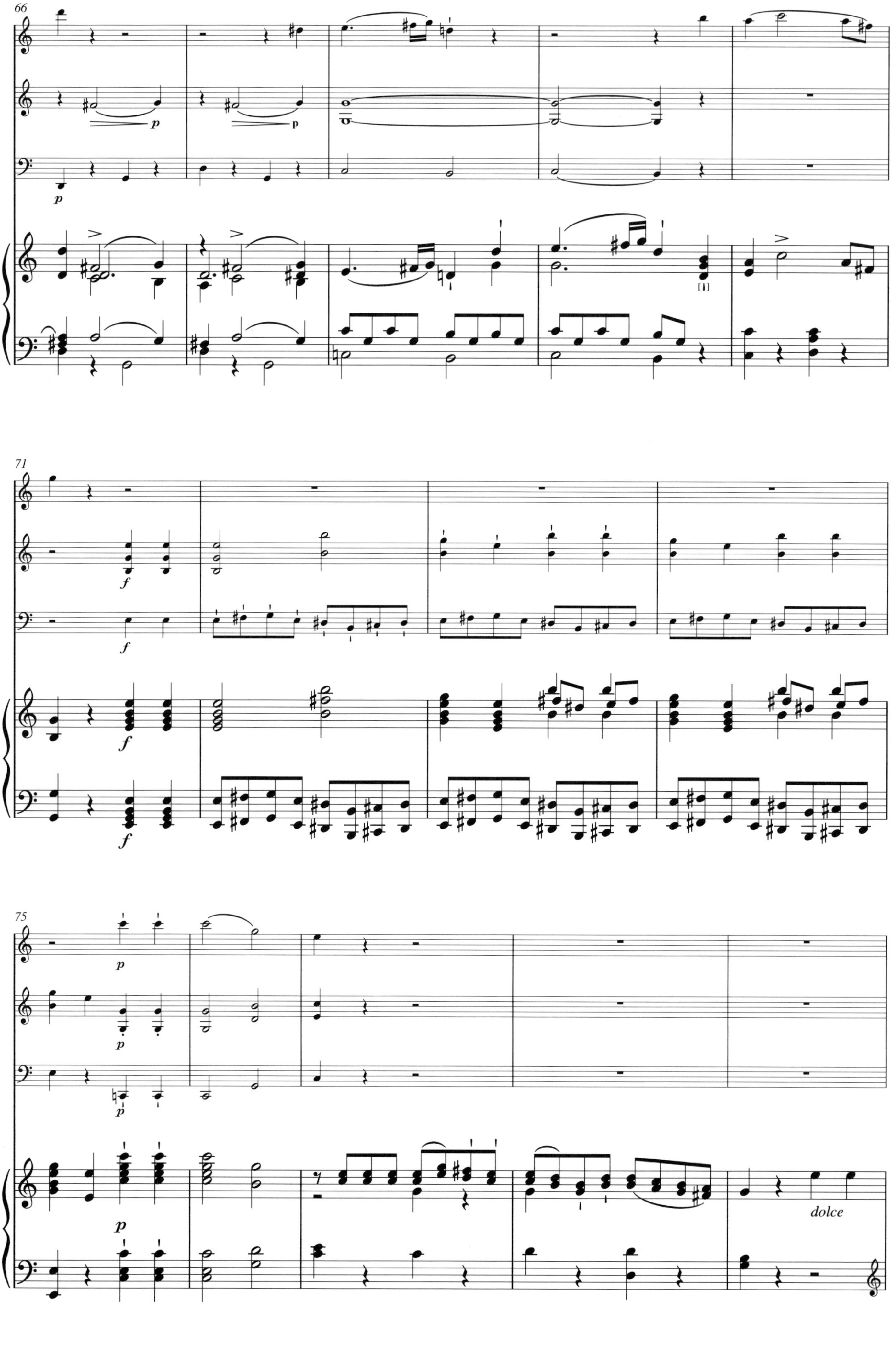
dolce

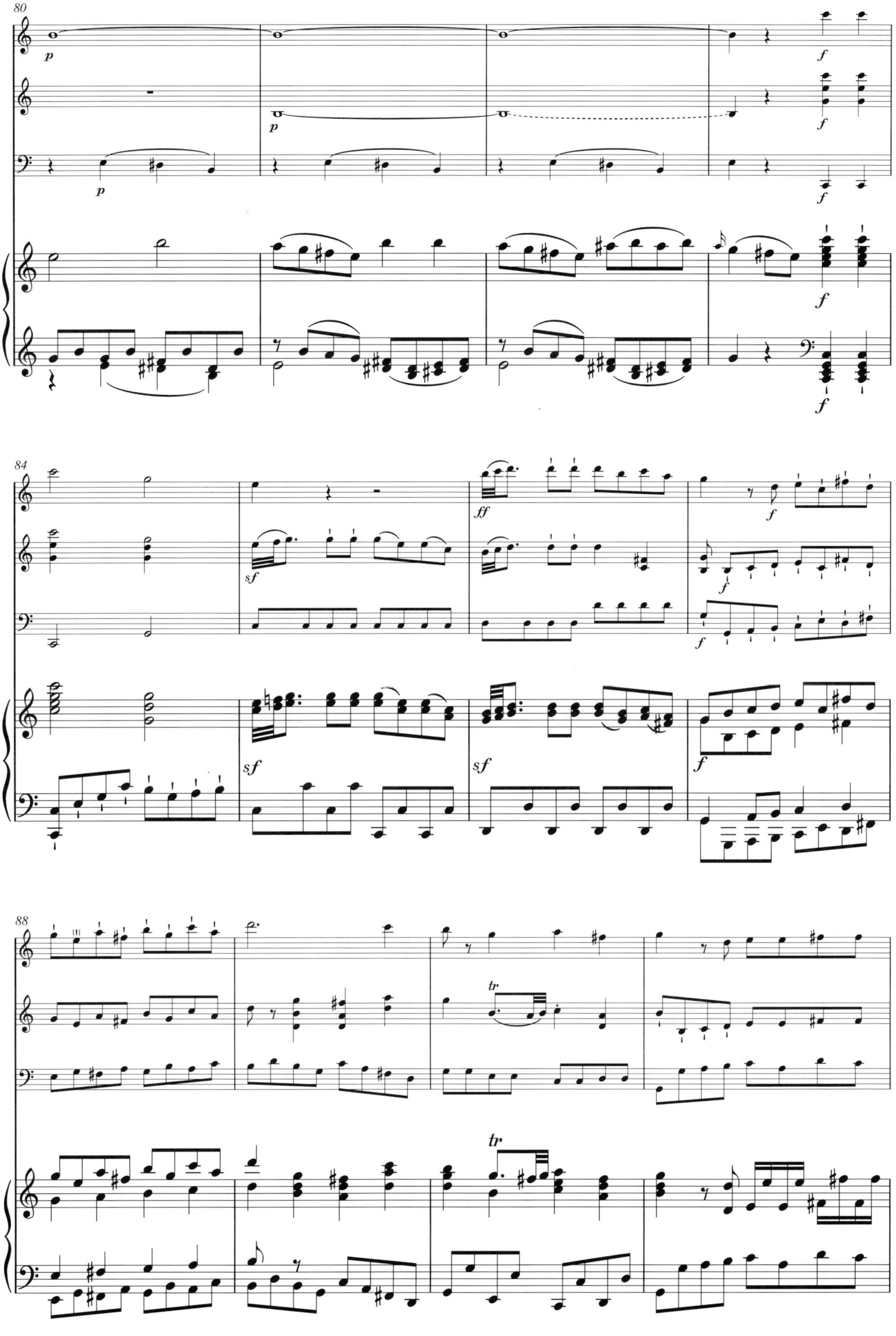

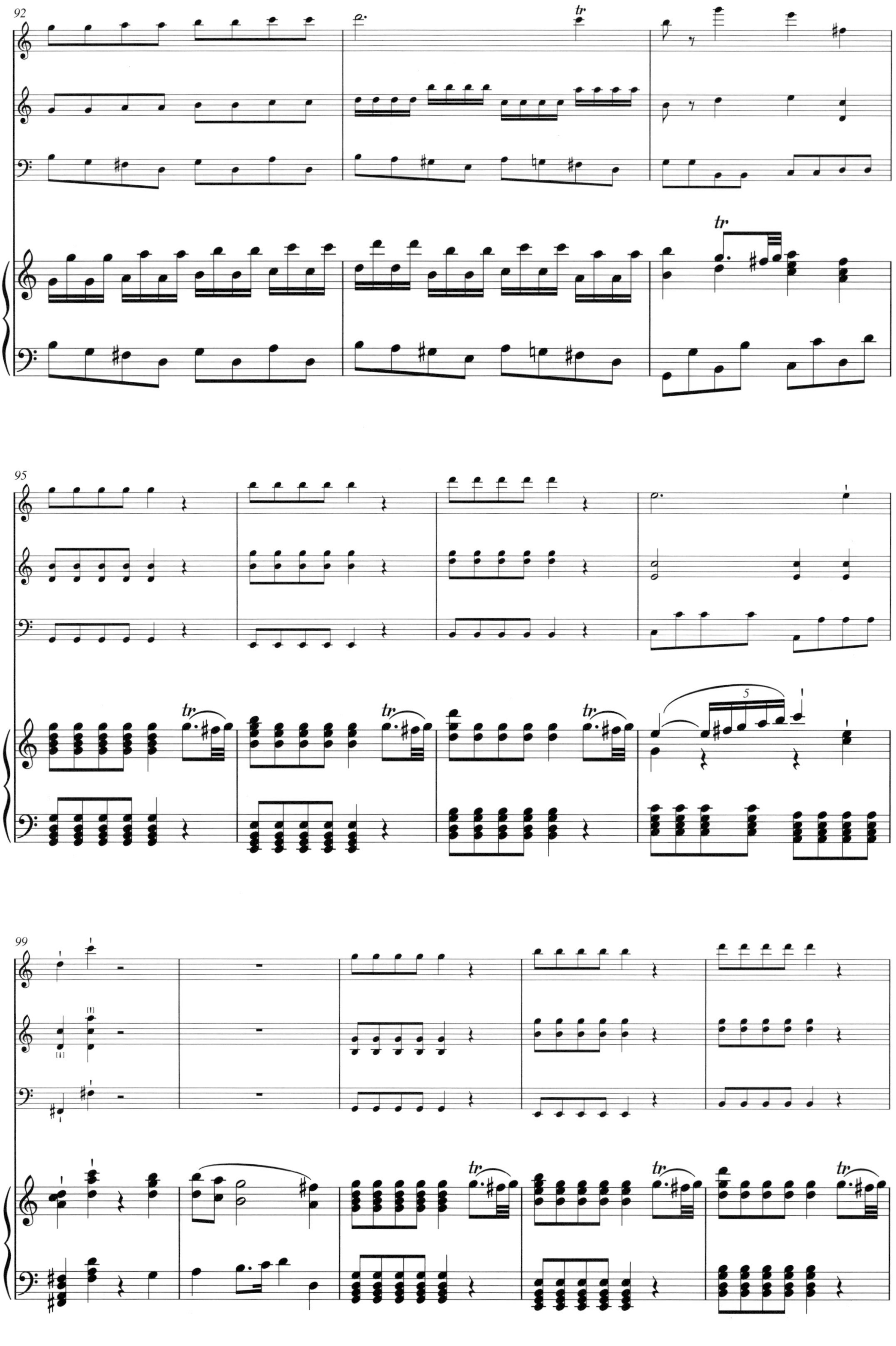
92
95
99

59

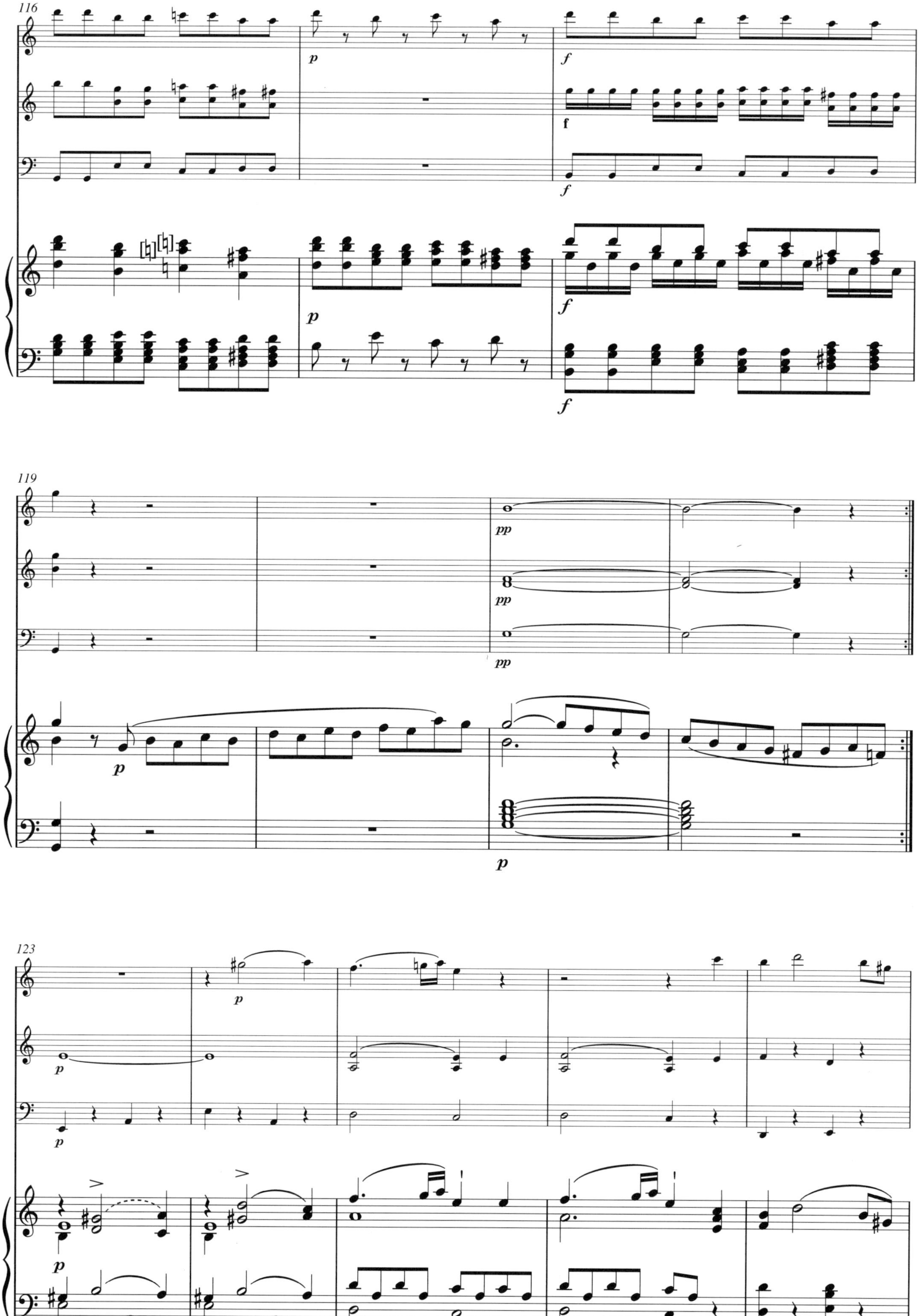
116
119
123

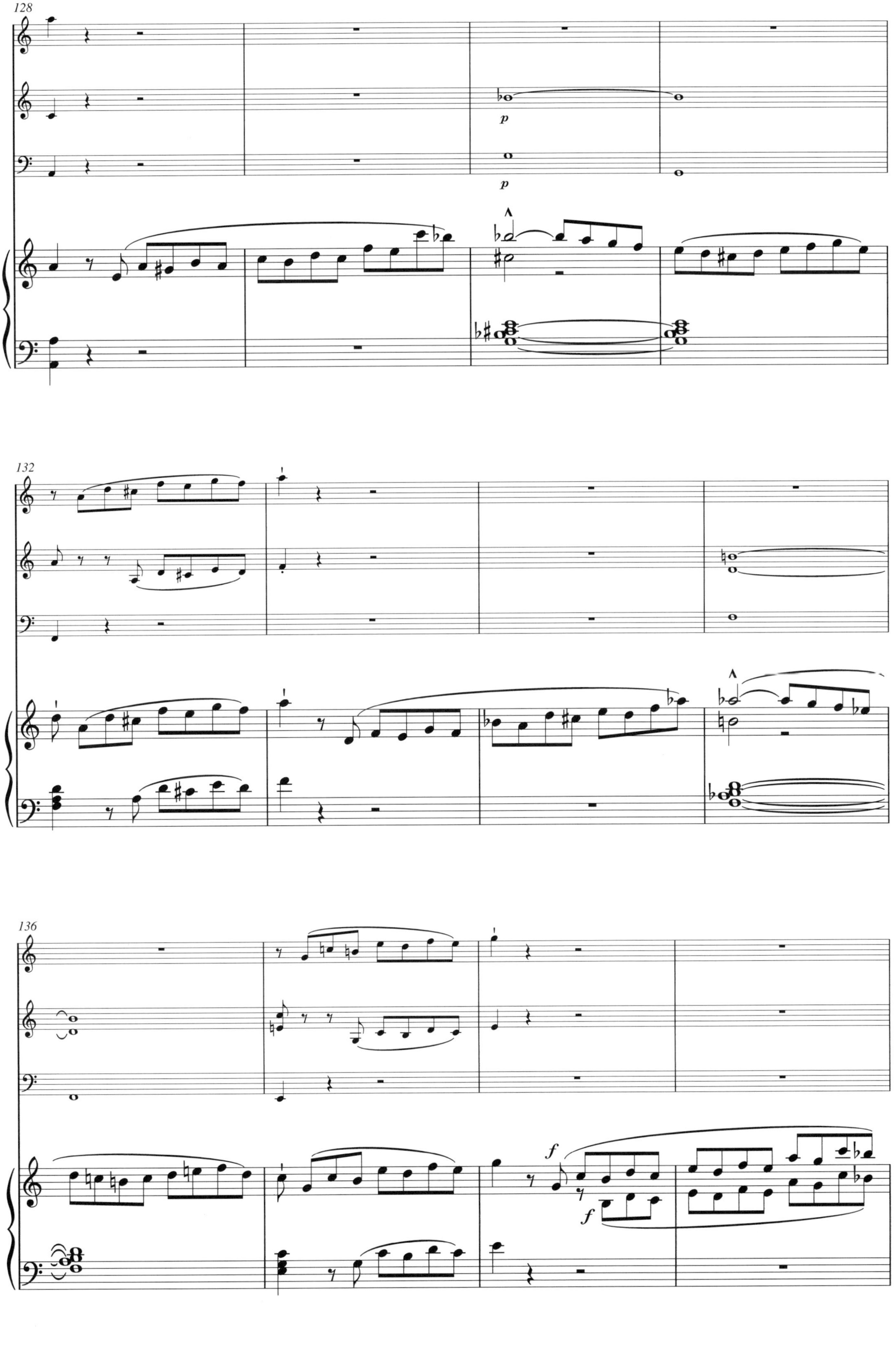
128
p
p
132
136
f
f

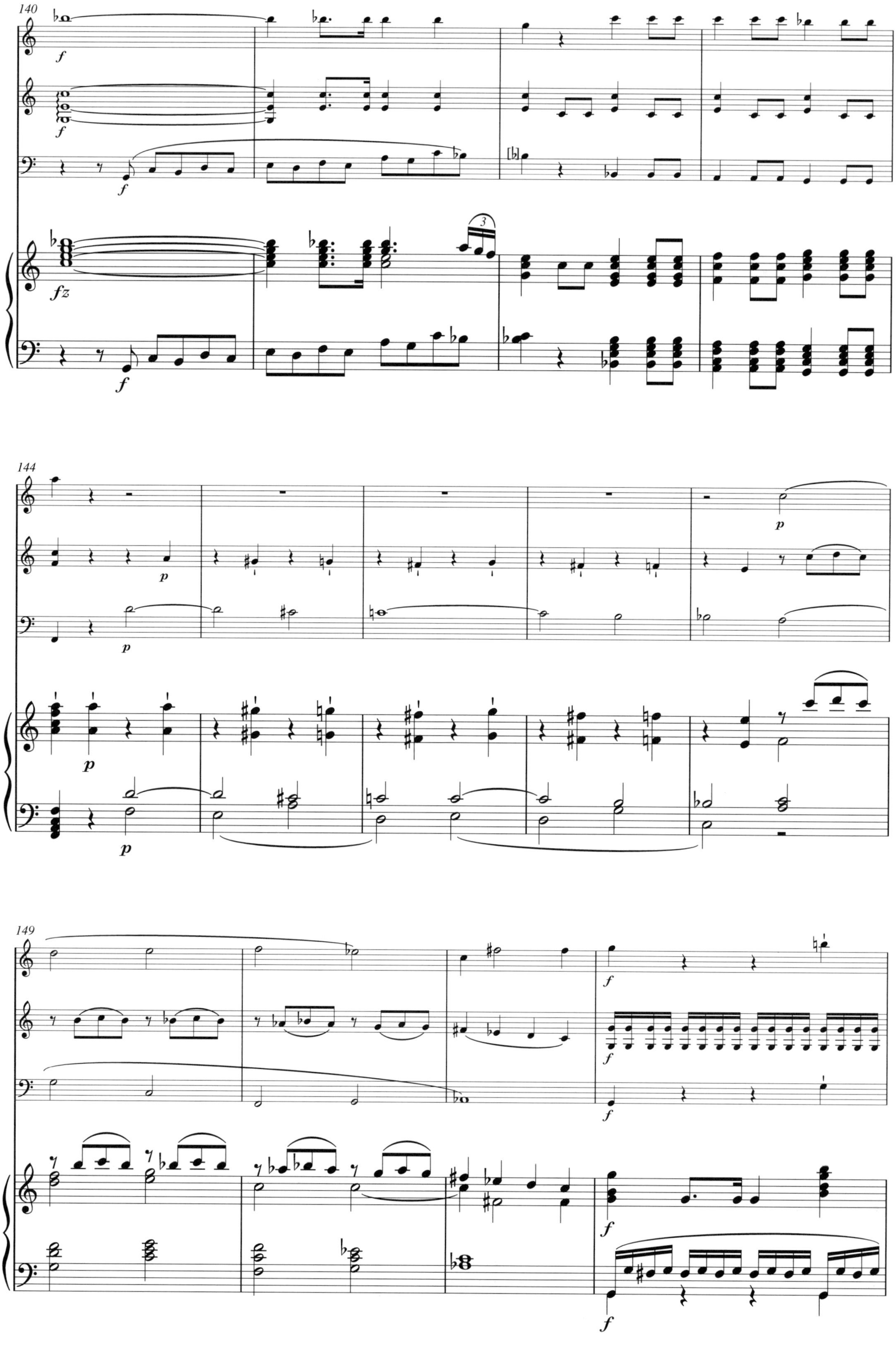
140
f
fz
3
144
p
149

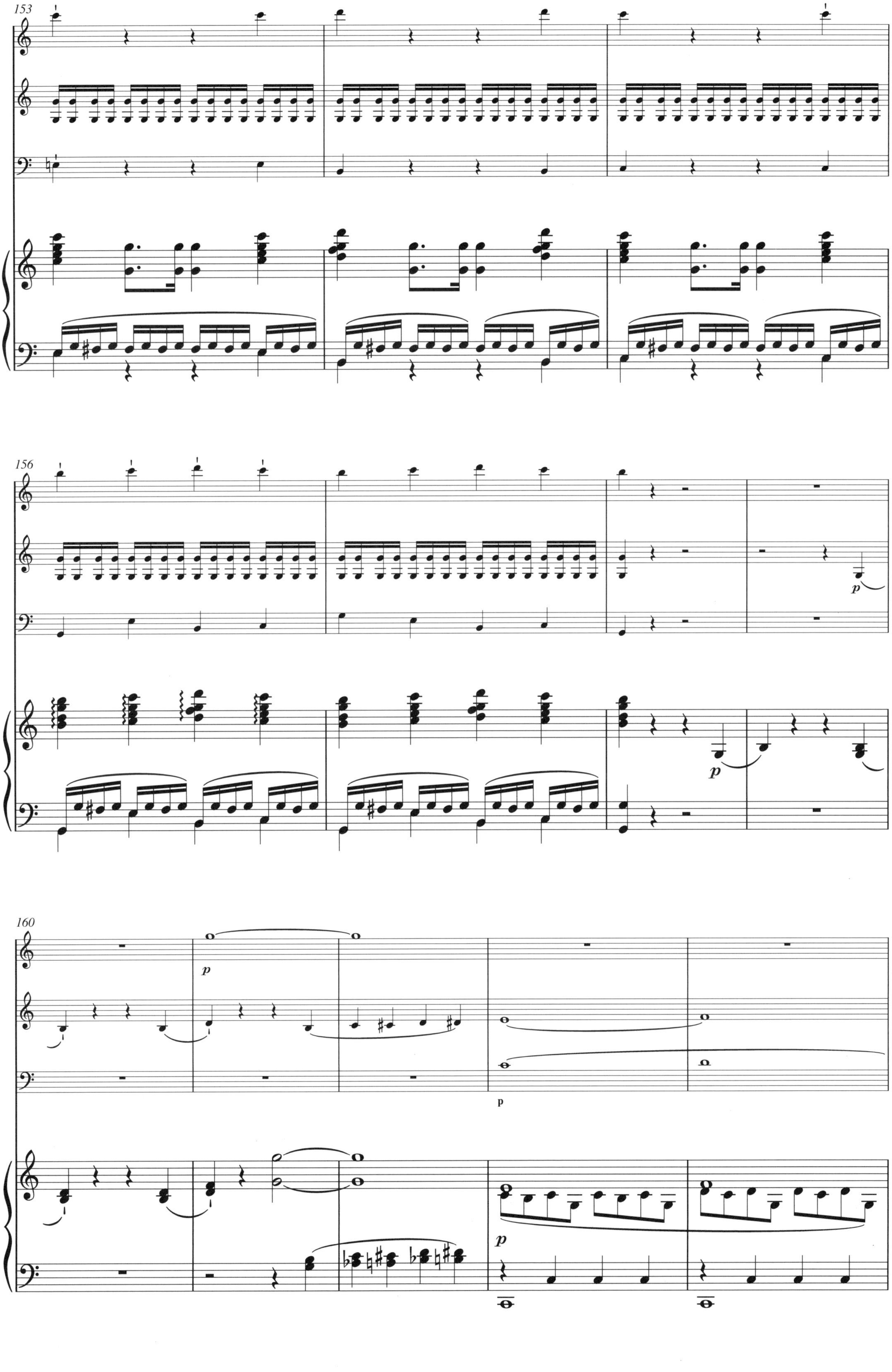
153
156
p
p
160
p
p
p

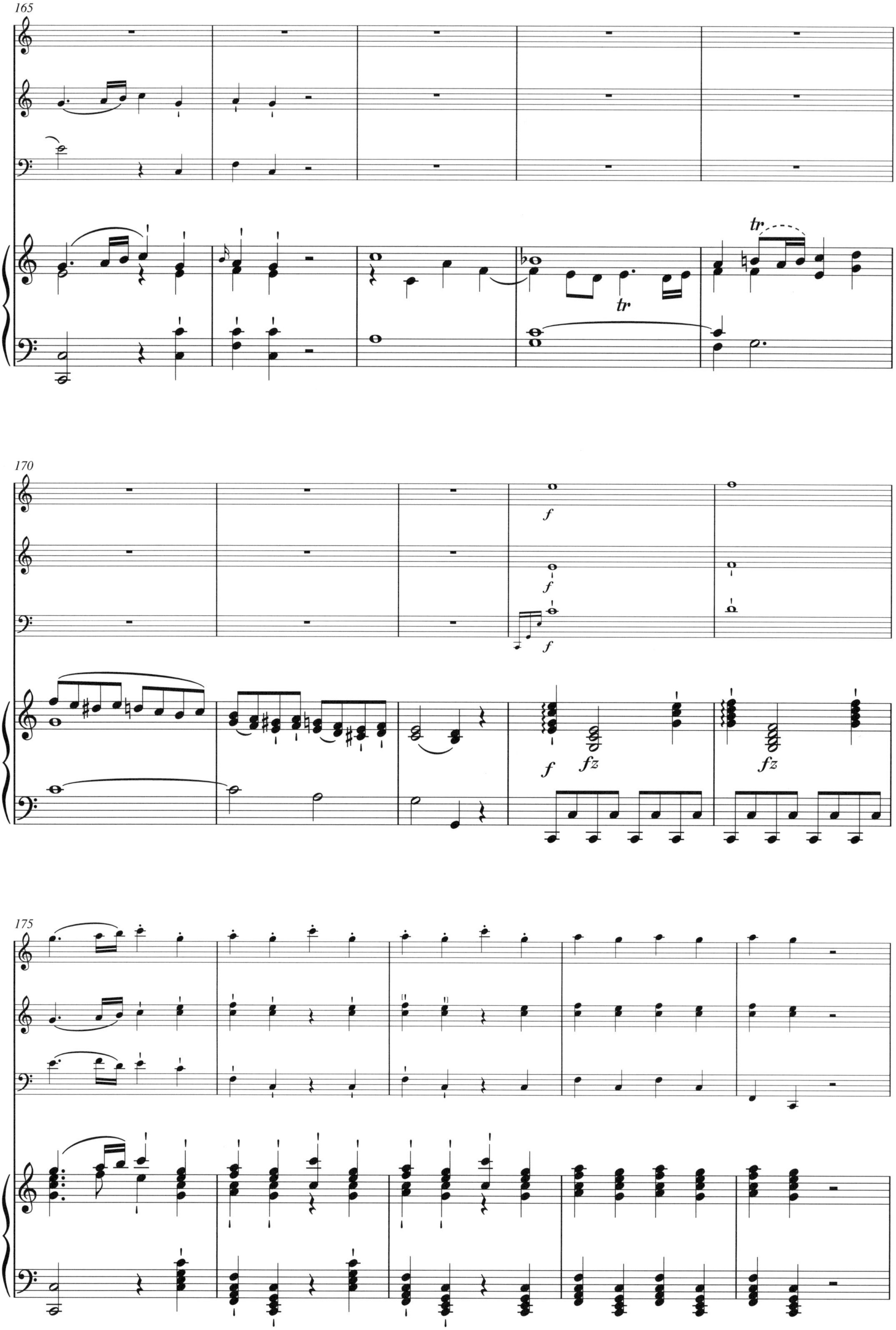
165
tr
tr
170
f
f
f
f
fz
fz
175

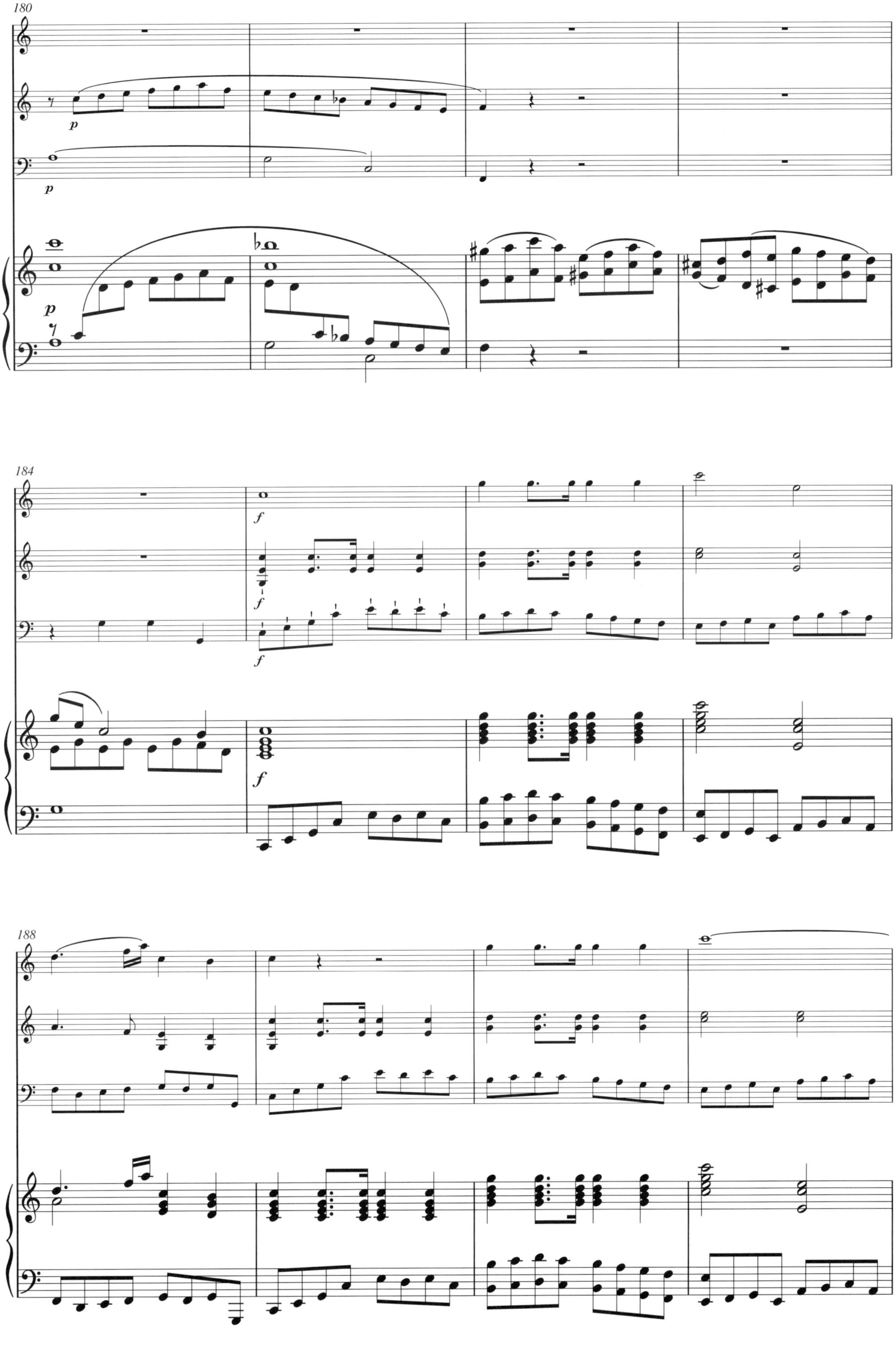
180
p
p
p
184
f
f
f
f
188

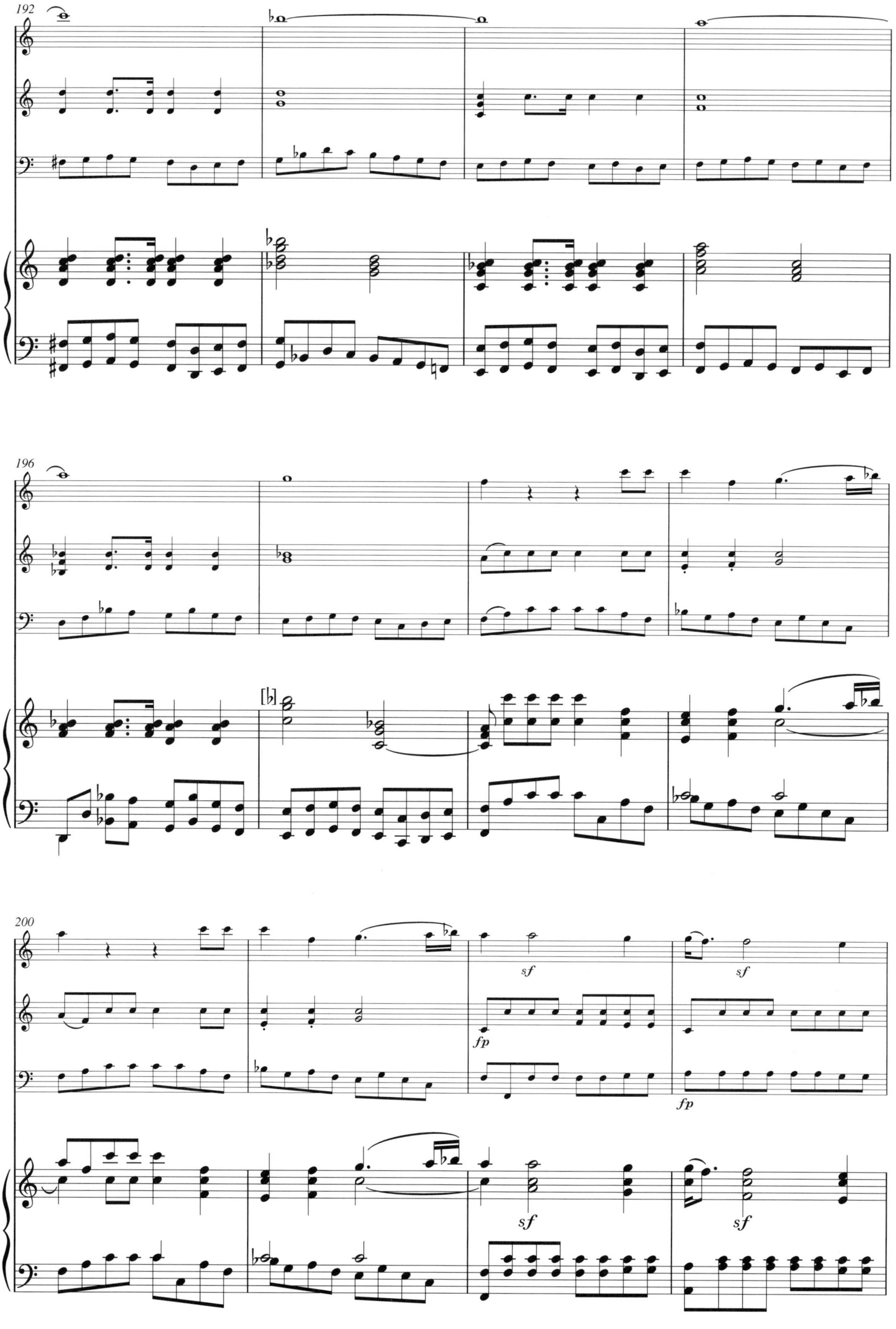
192
196
200
sf
sf
fp
fp
sf
sf

67

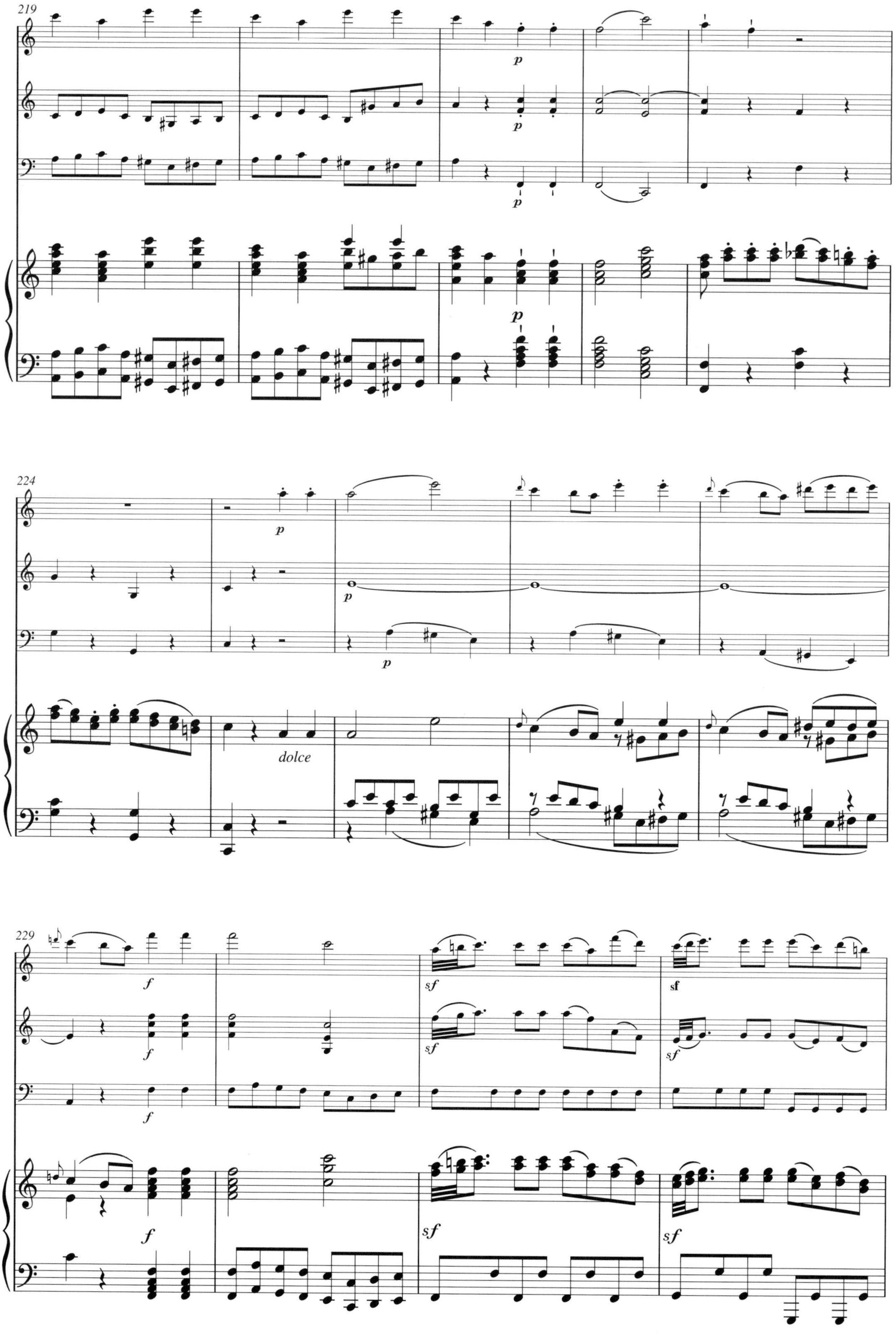
219
p
224
p
dolce
229
f
sf

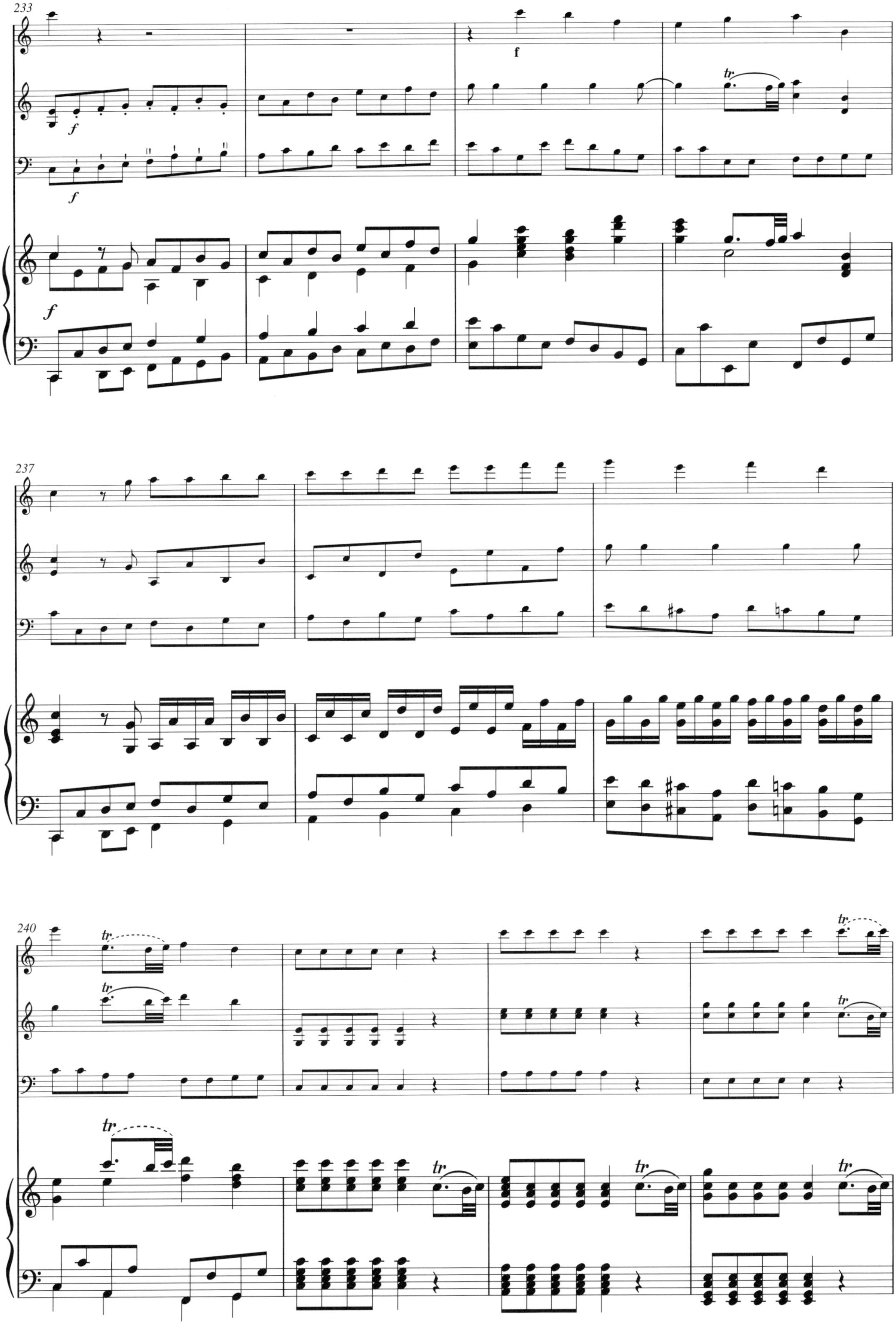
233
f
f
f
f
f
tr
237
240
tr
tr
tr
tr
tr
tr
tr

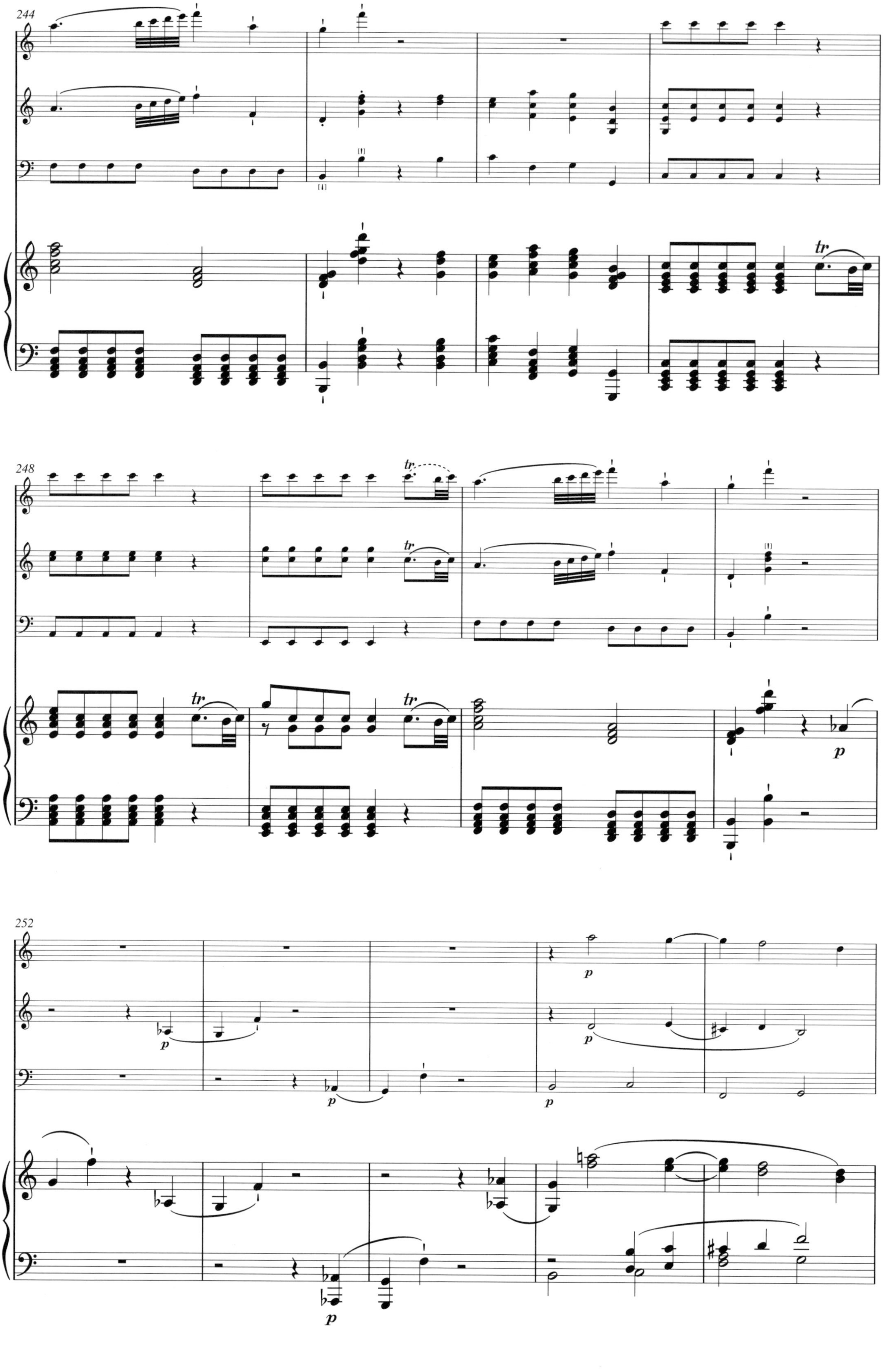
244
tr
248
tr
tr
tr
[!]
[!]
[!]
p
252
p
p
p
p
p

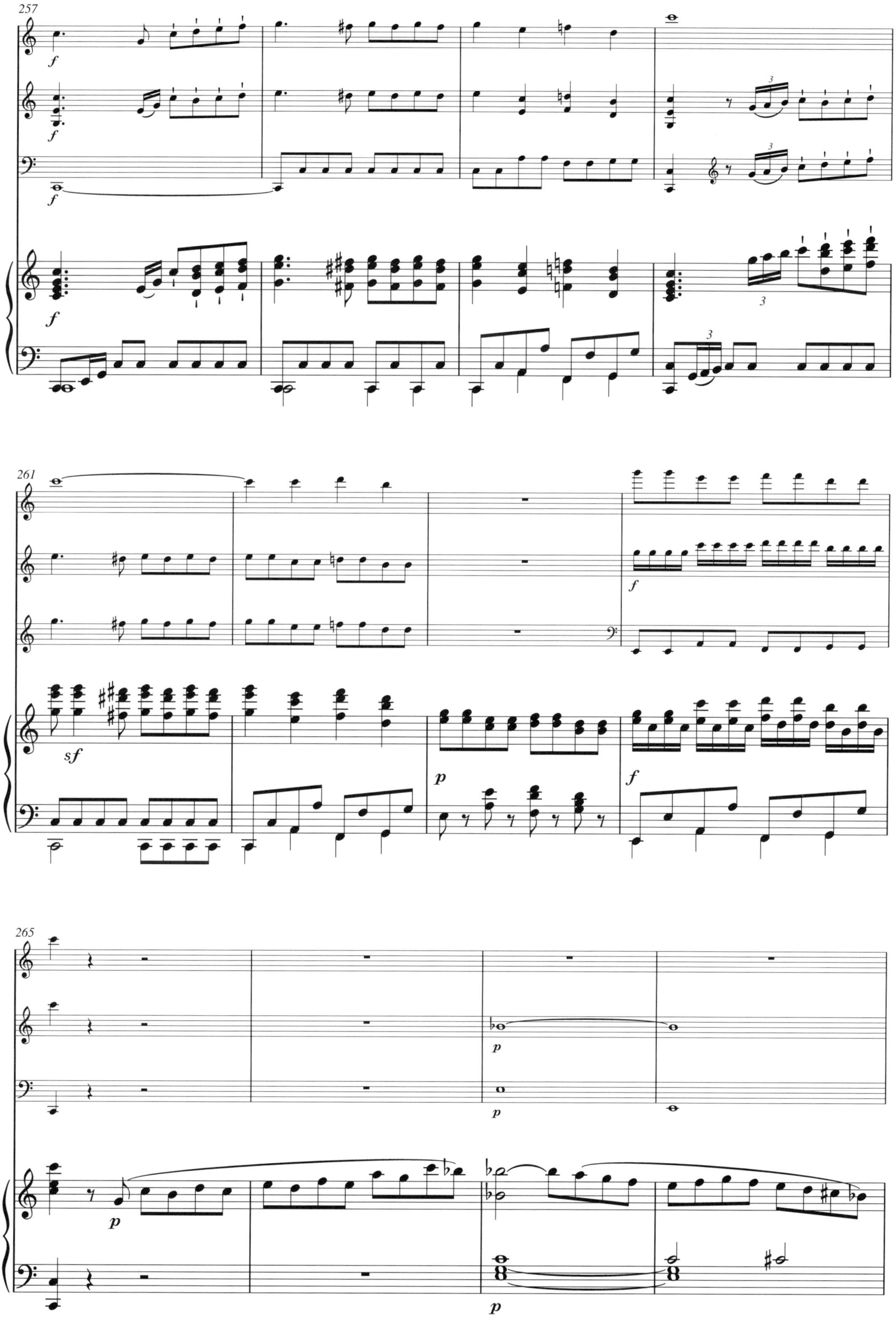
257
261
265

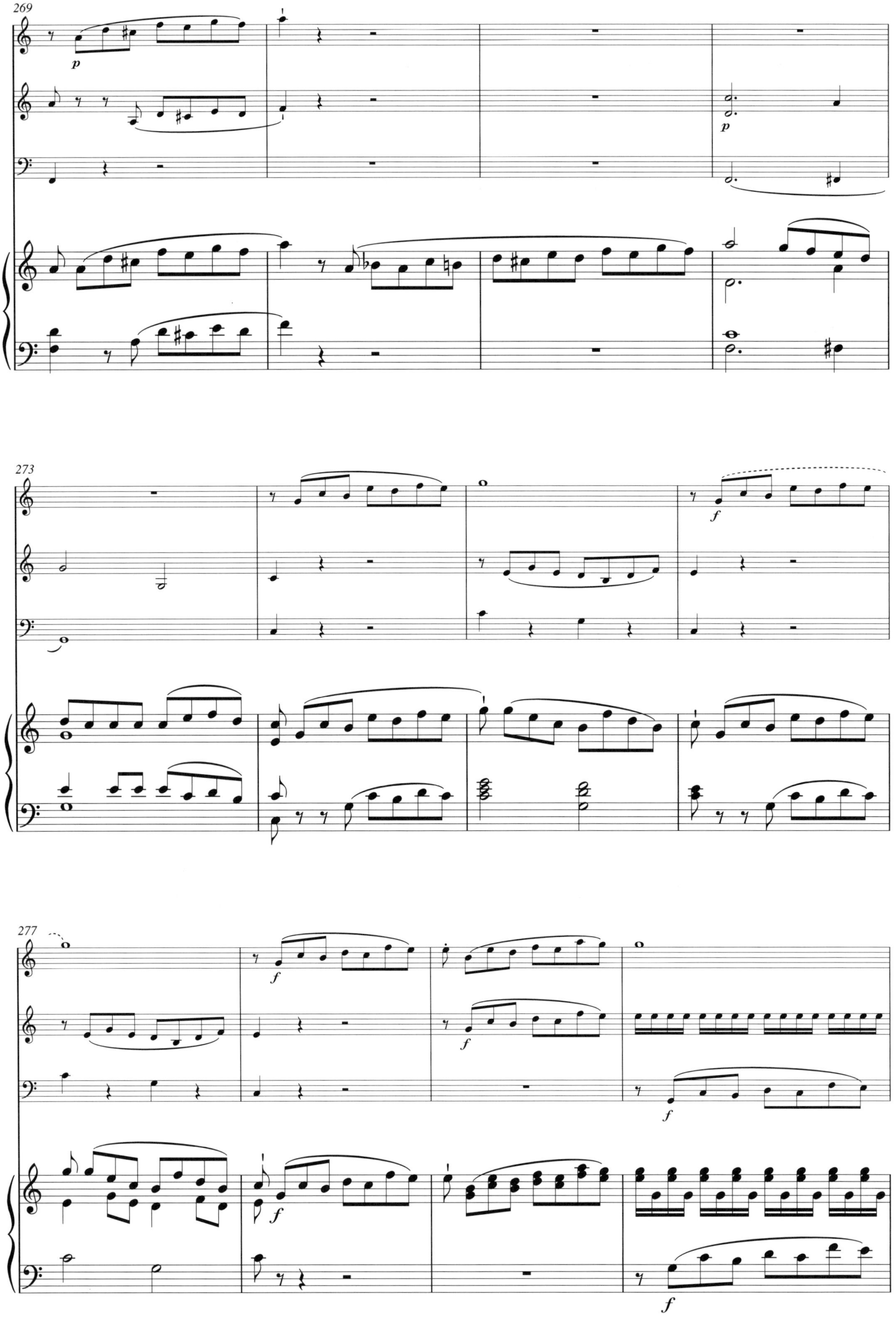
269
p
p
273
f
277
f
f
f
f
f

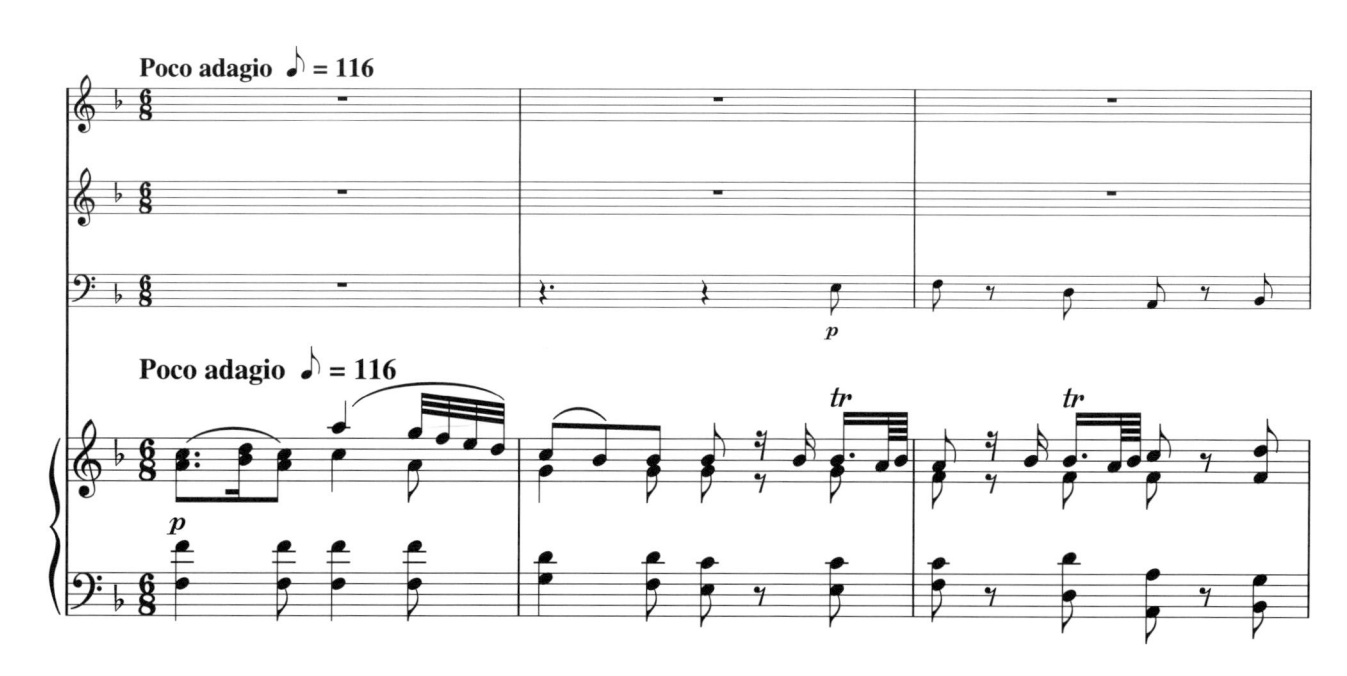

II

Poco adagio ♪ = 116

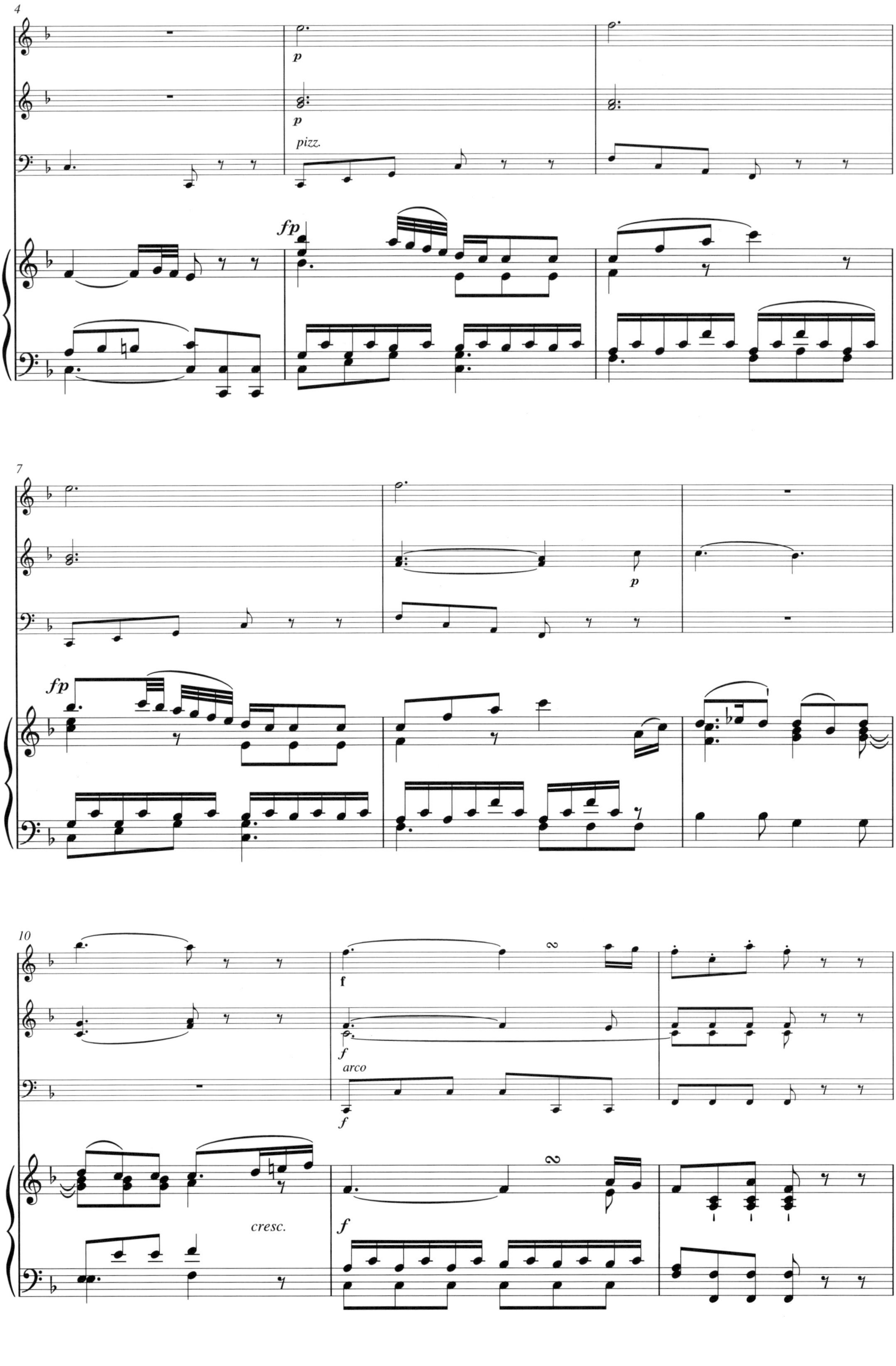
4
p
p
pizz.
fp
7
fp
p
10
f
f
arco
f
cresc.
f

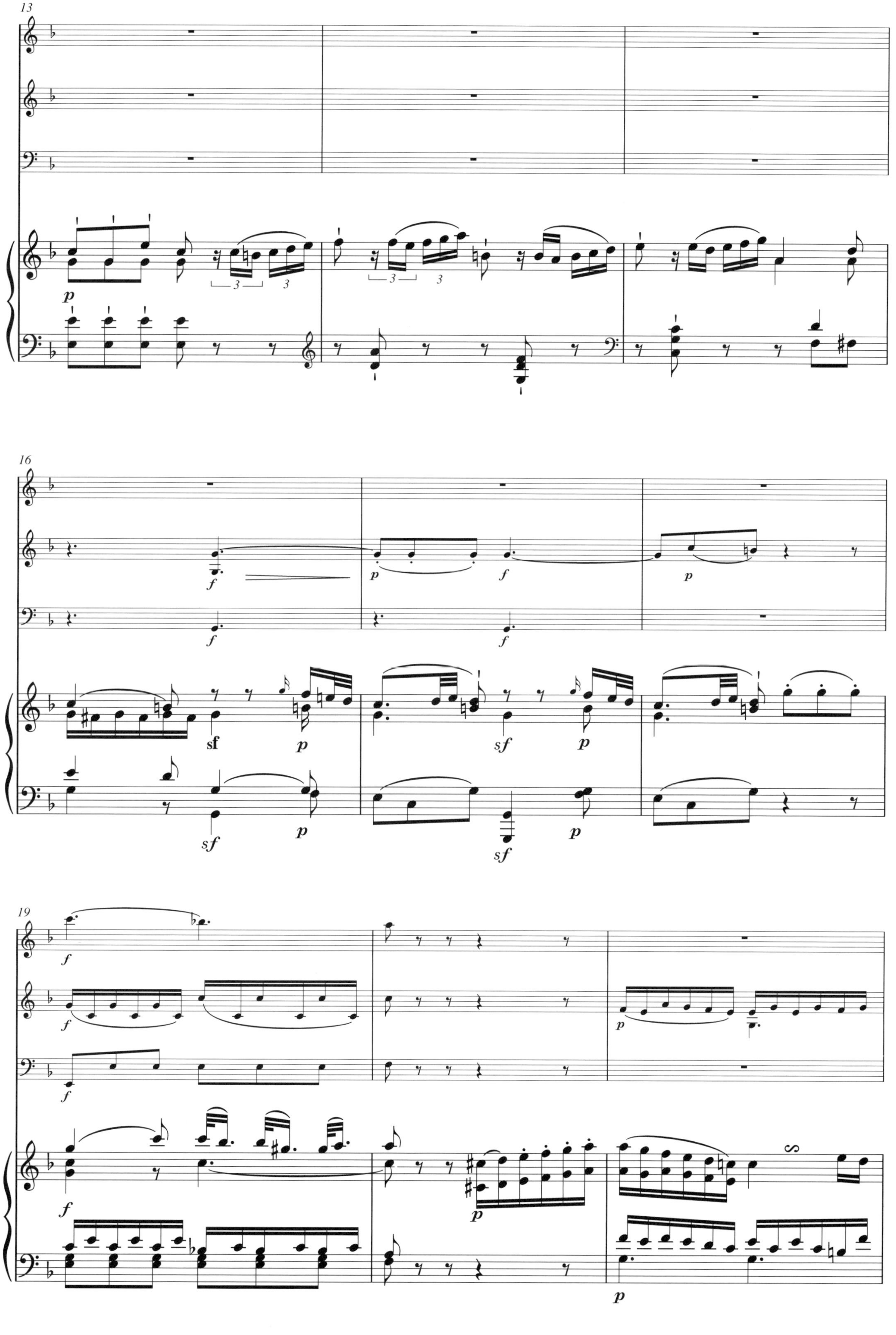
13
p
16
f
p
f
p
f
f
sf
p
sf
p
sf
p
sf
p
19
f
f
f
f
p
p
p

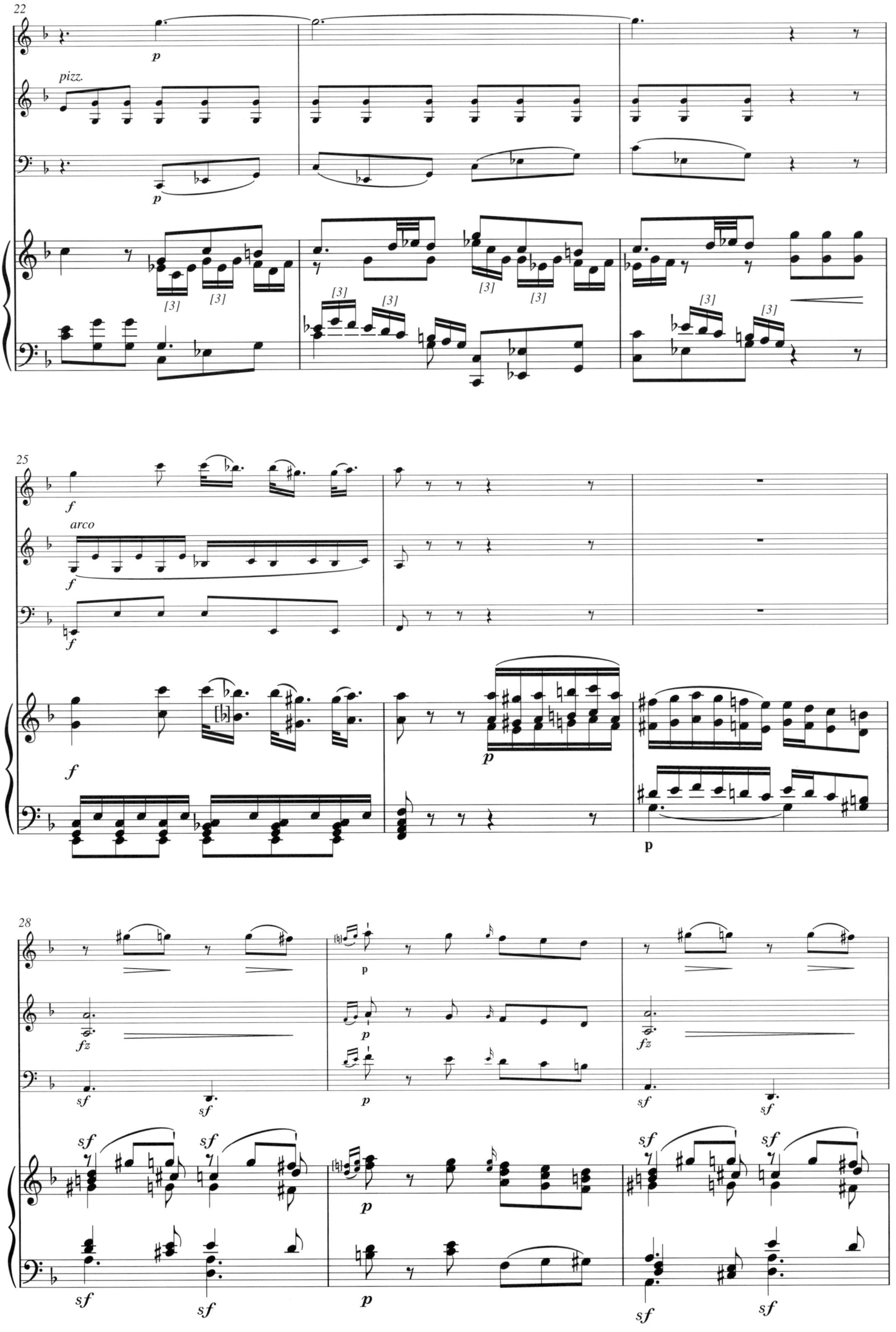
22
pizz.
25
arco
28

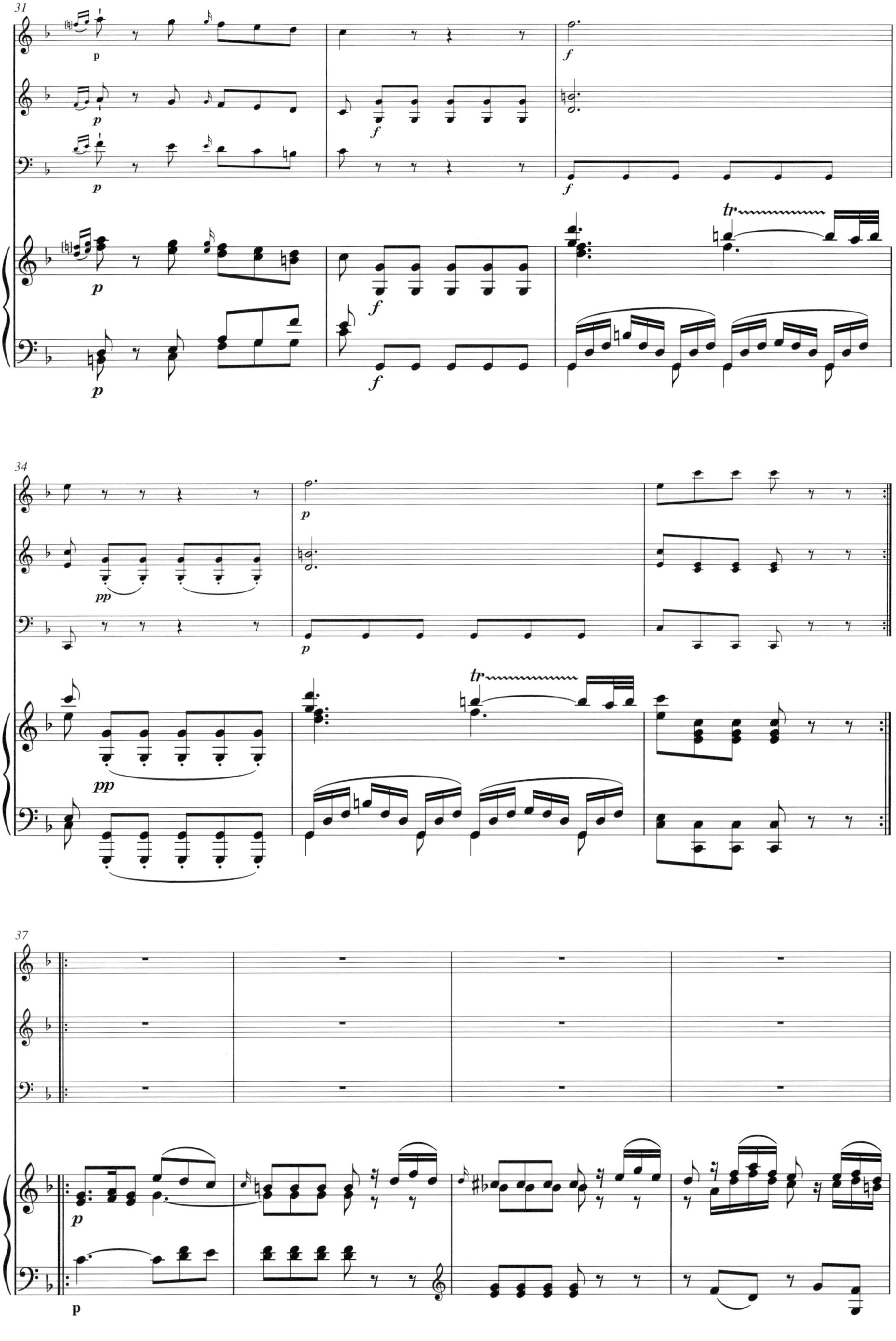
31
34
37
tr
p
f
pp

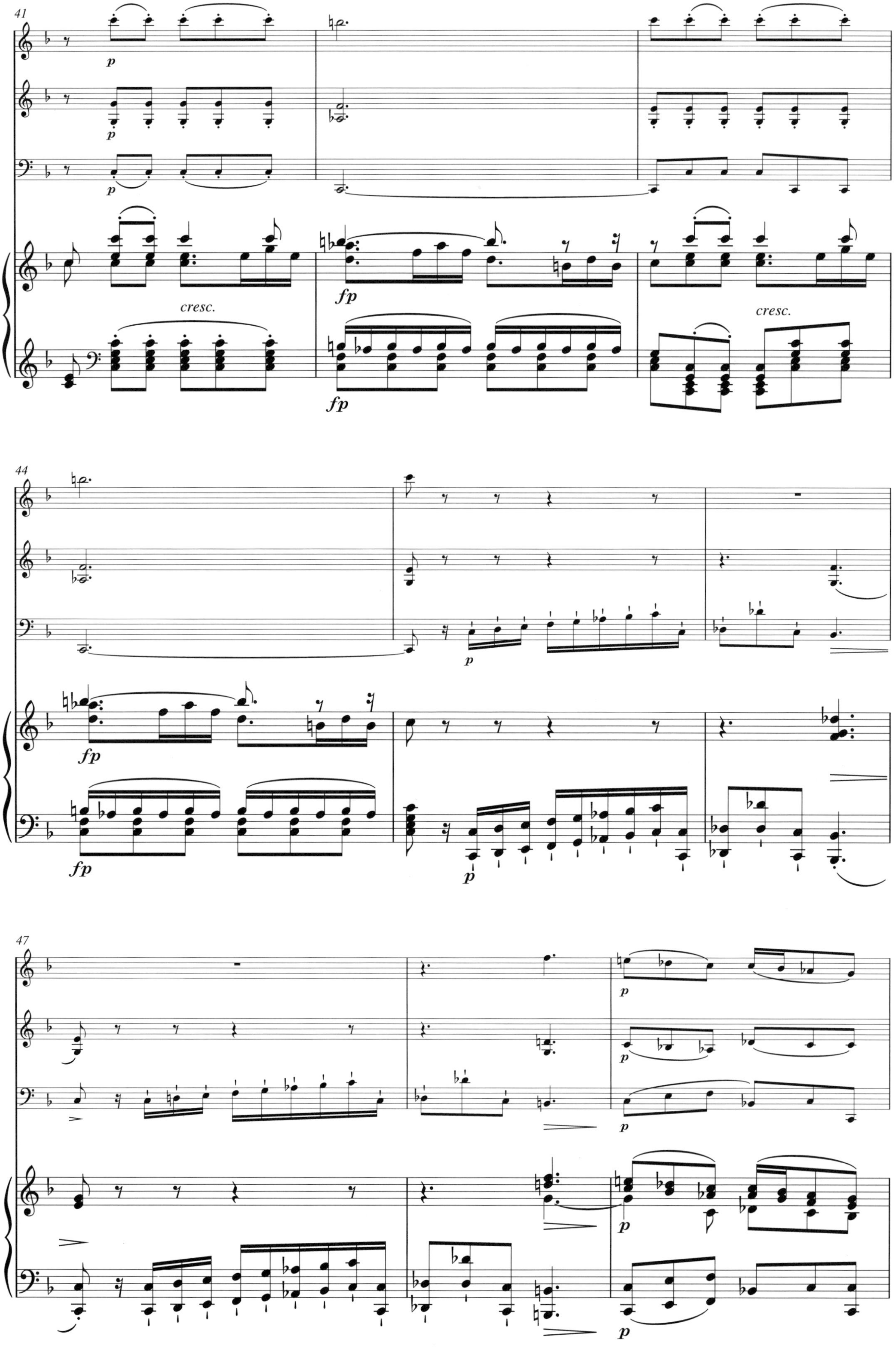
41
p
cresc.
fp
44
47

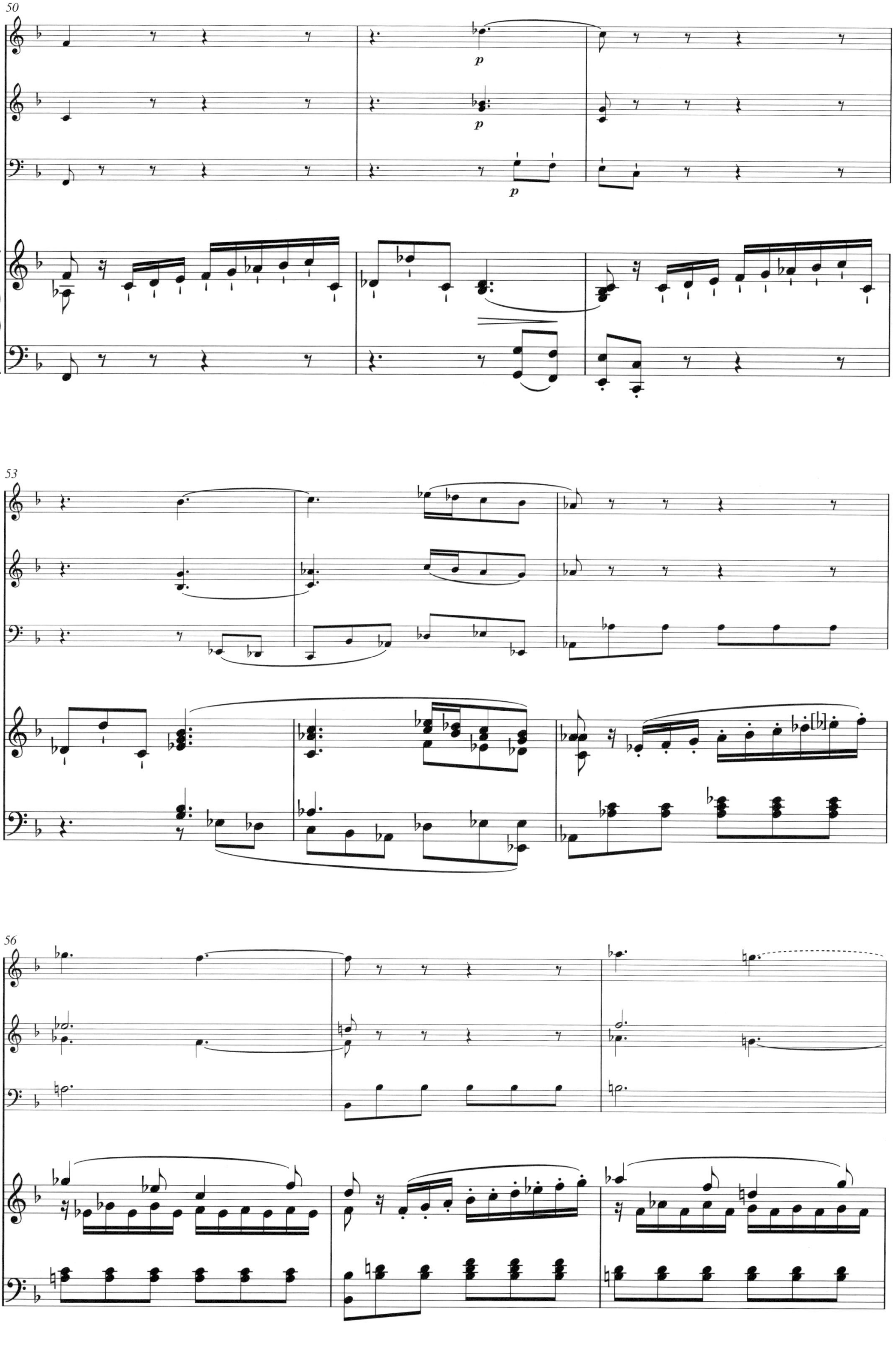
50
p
p
p
53
56

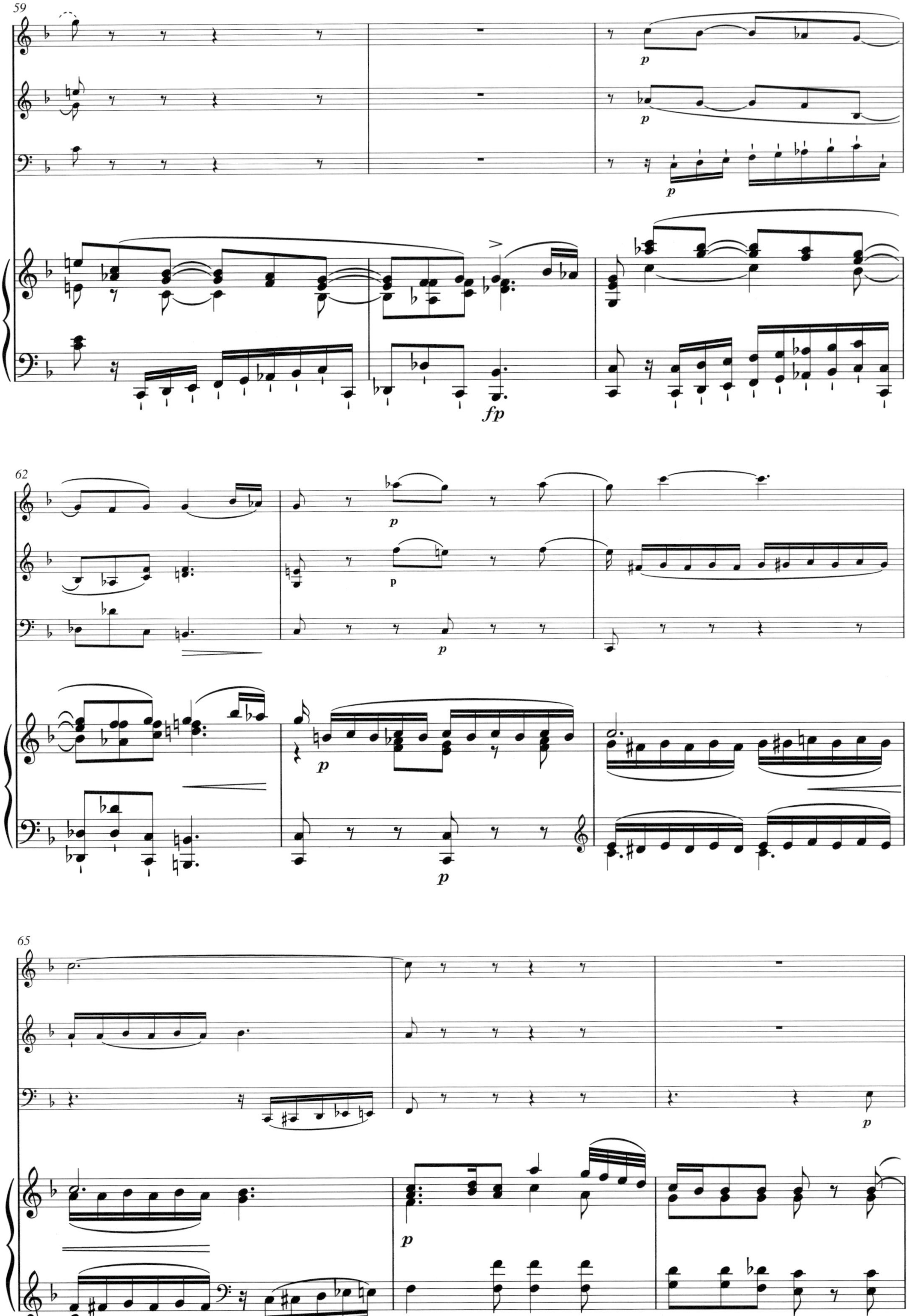
59
p
p
p
fp
62
p
p
p
p
p
65
p
p

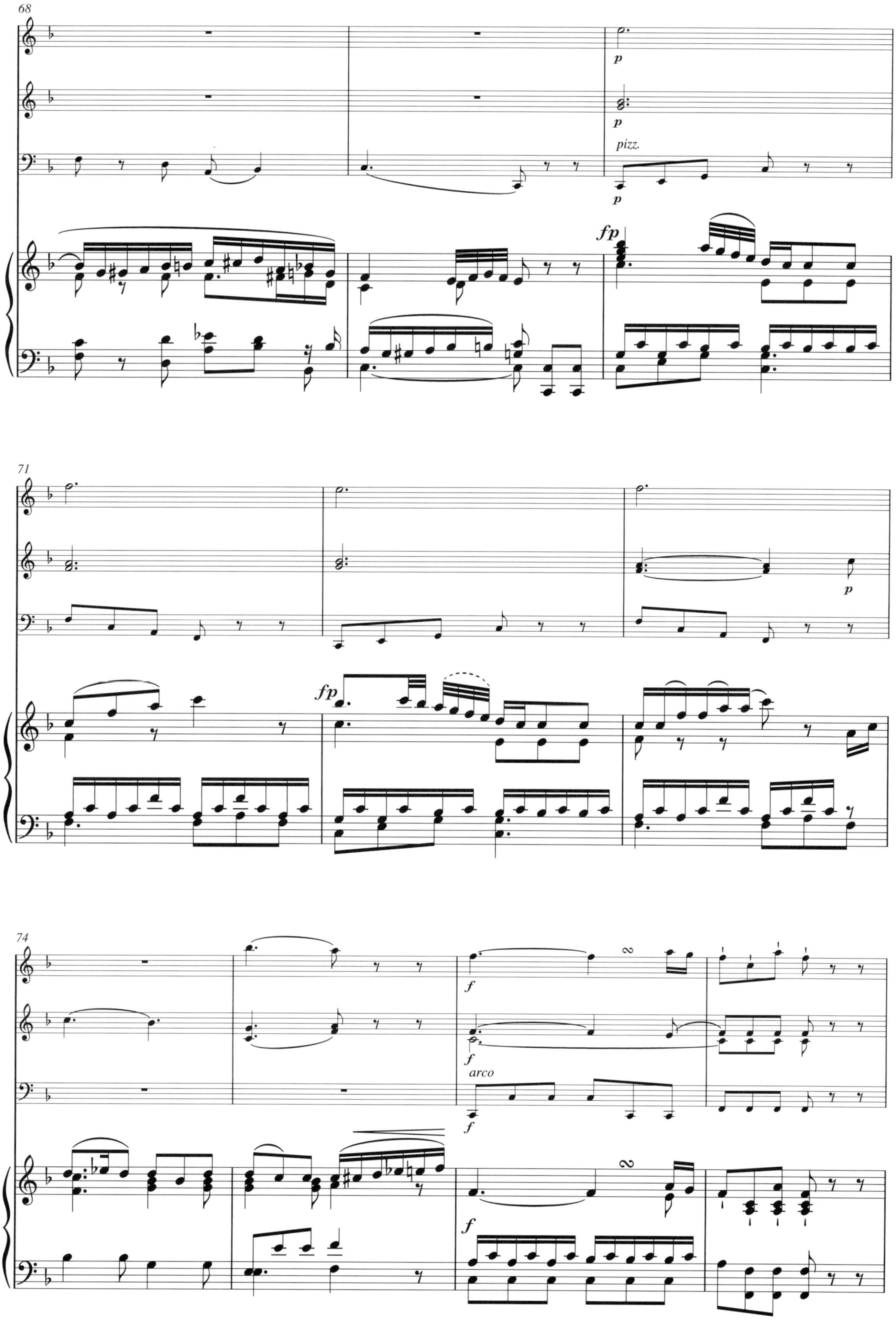
68
pizz.
71
74
arco

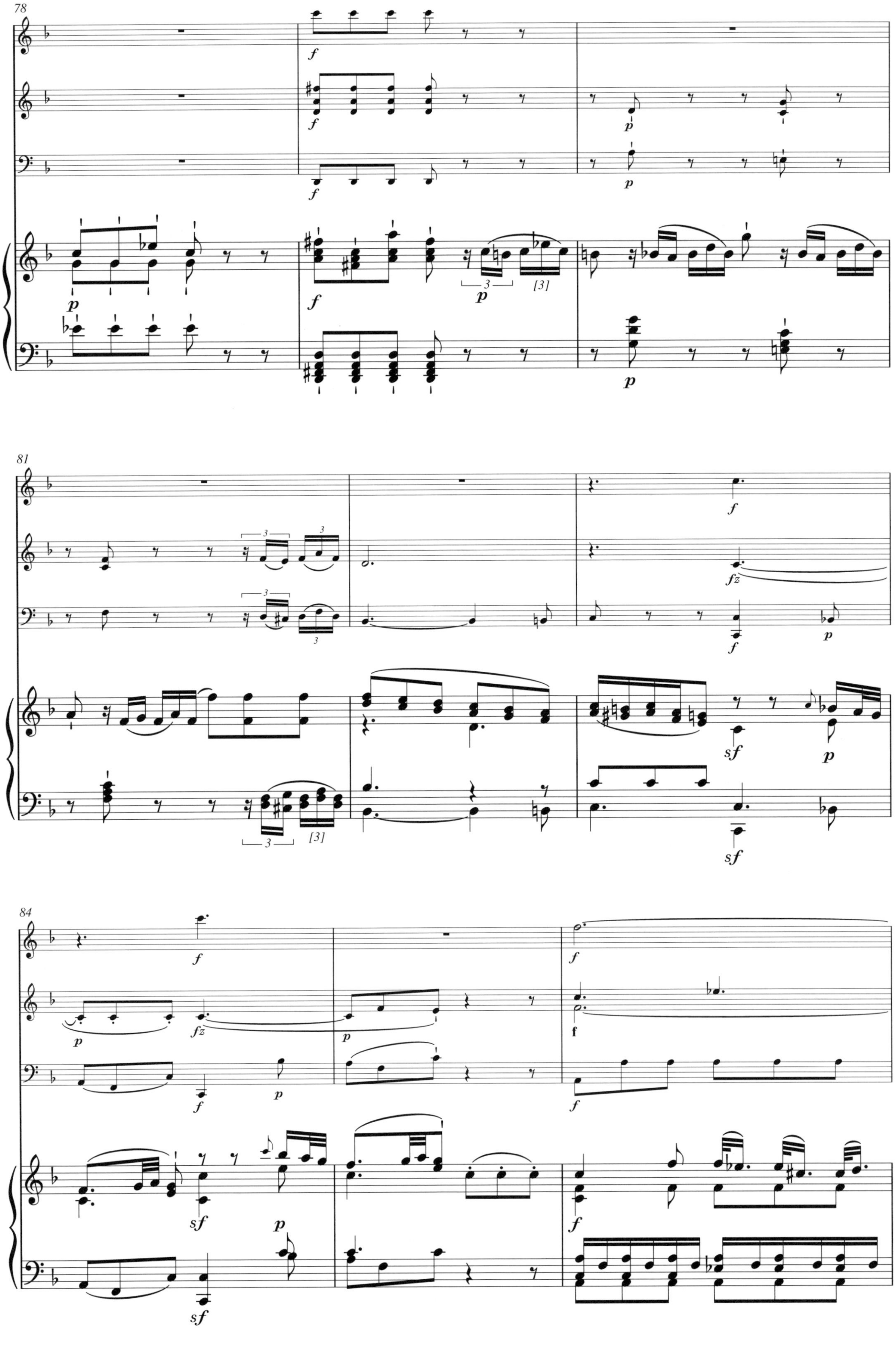
78
81
84

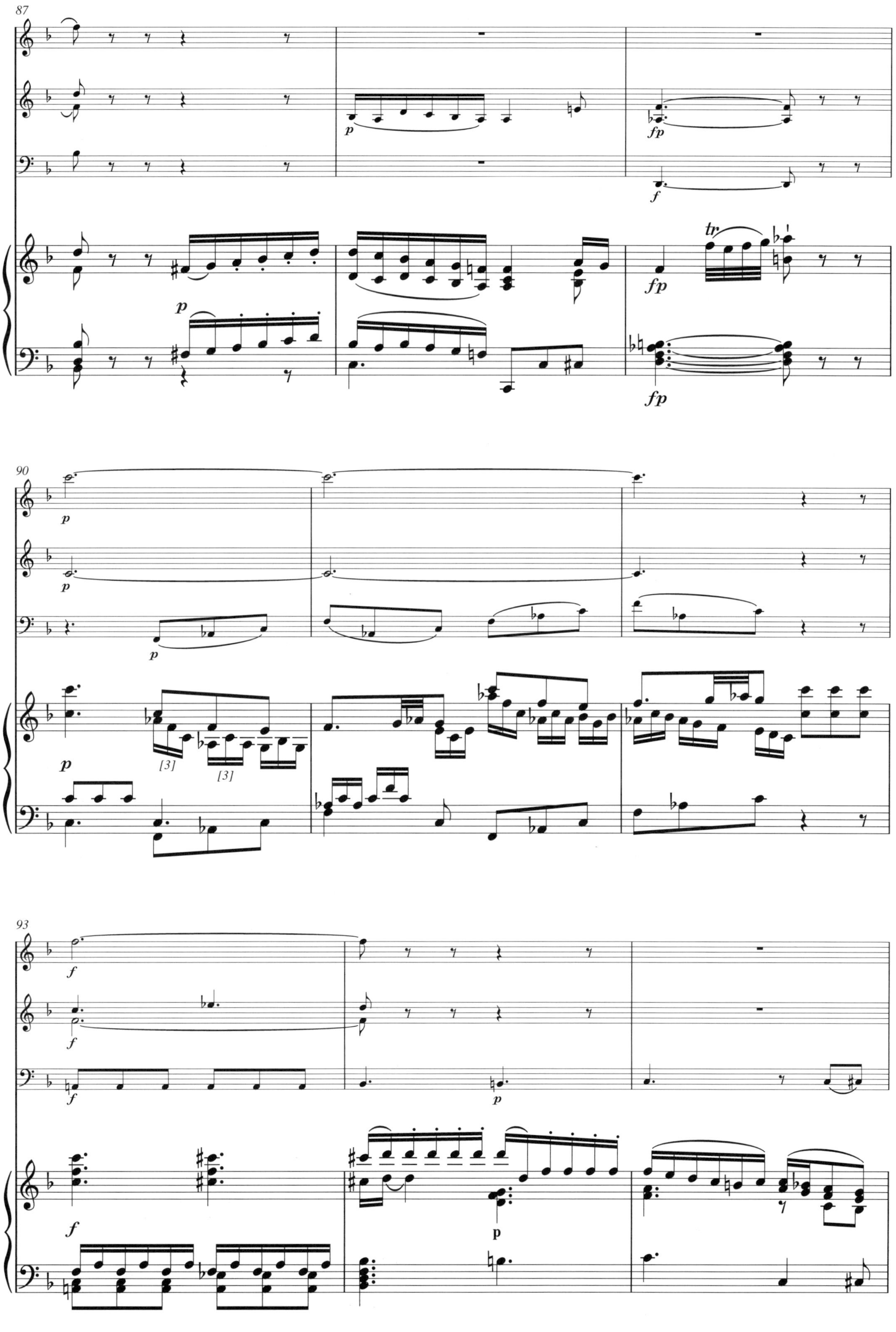
87
90
93

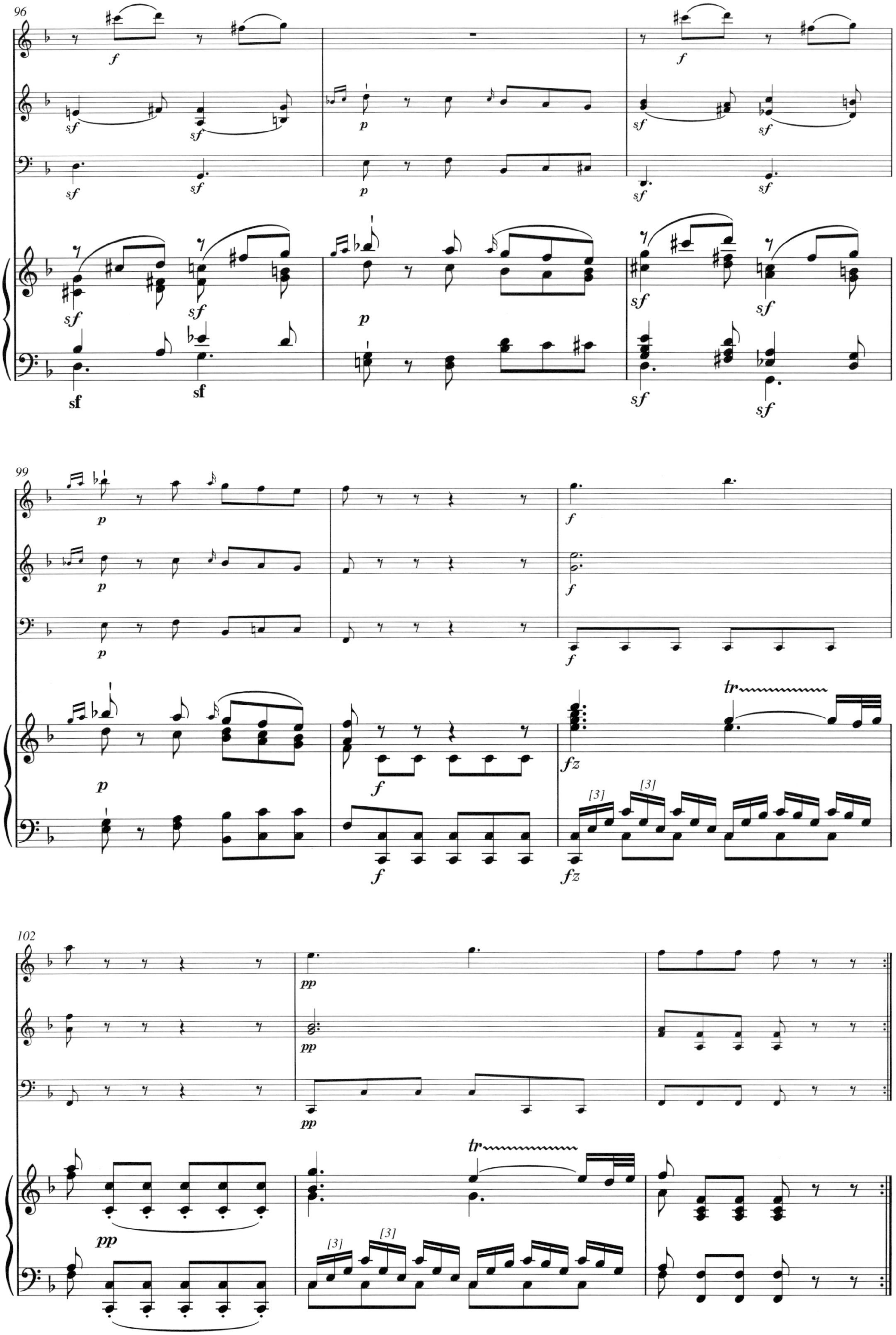
96
99
102

III

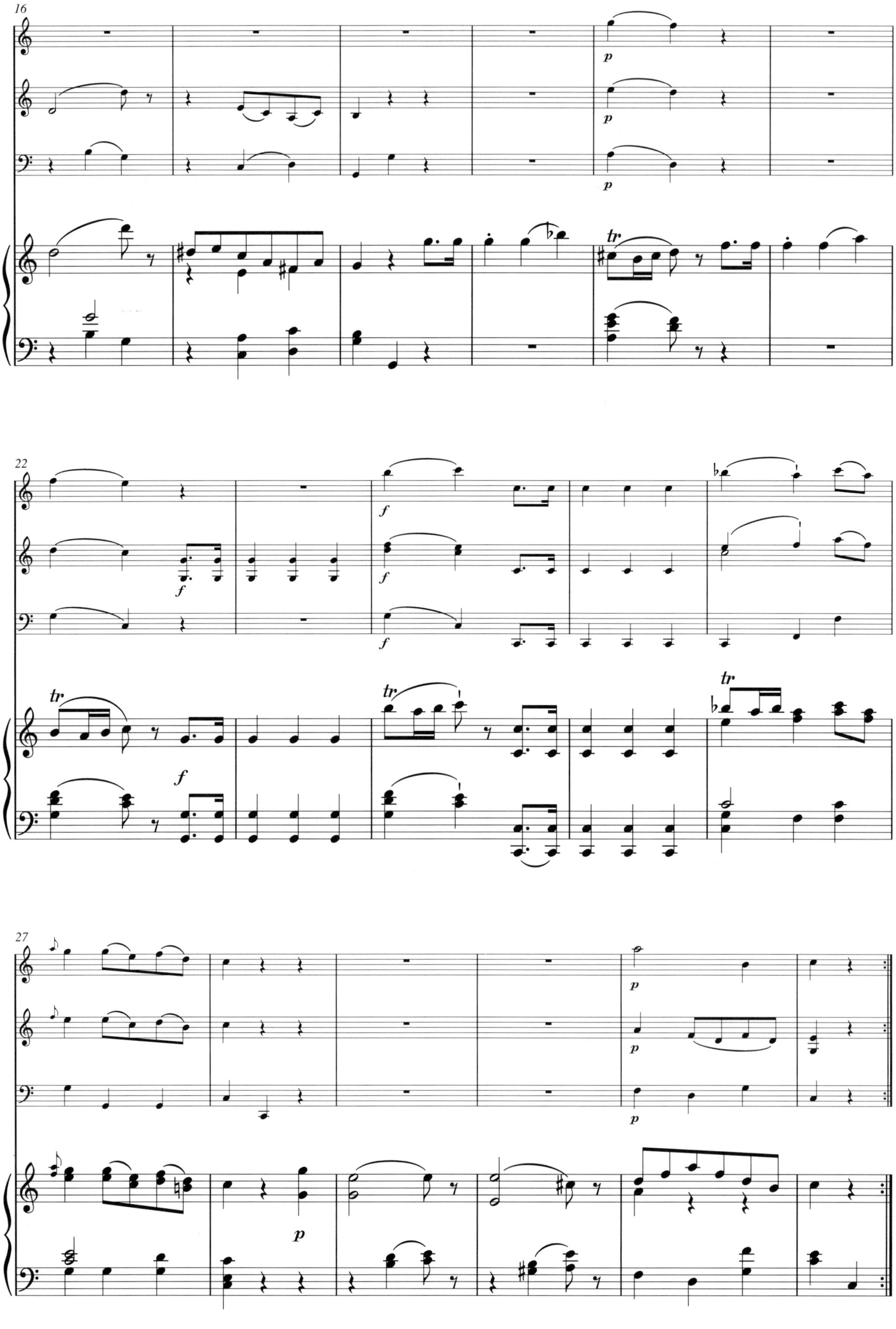
16
22
27

87

Menuetto da capo

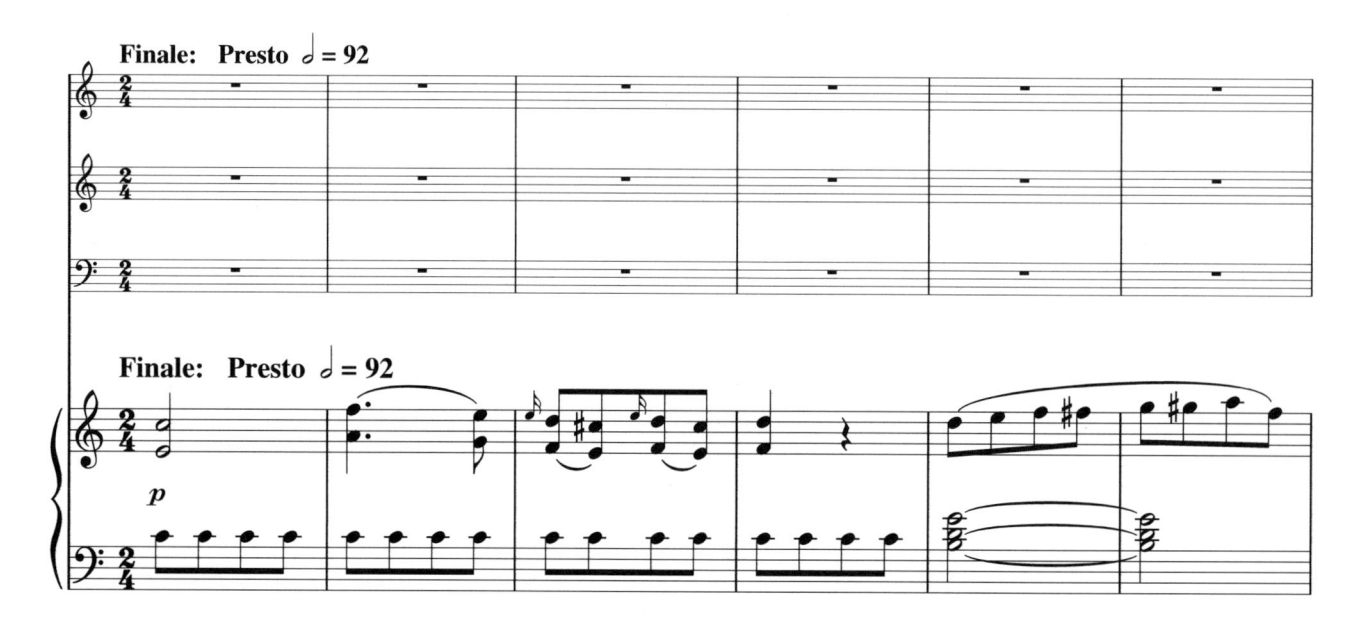

Menuetto da capo

IV

Finale: Presto ♩ = 92

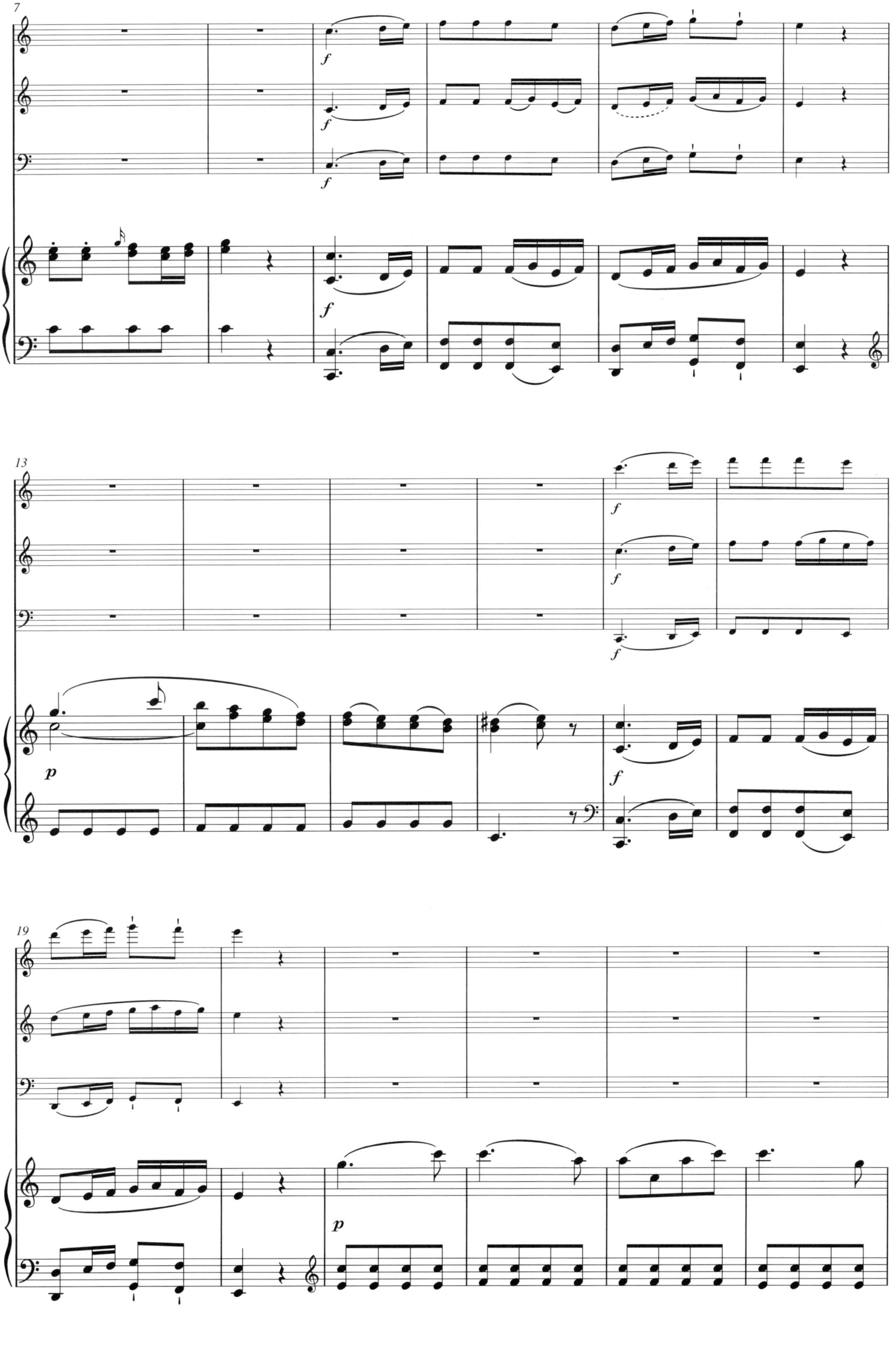
7
13
19

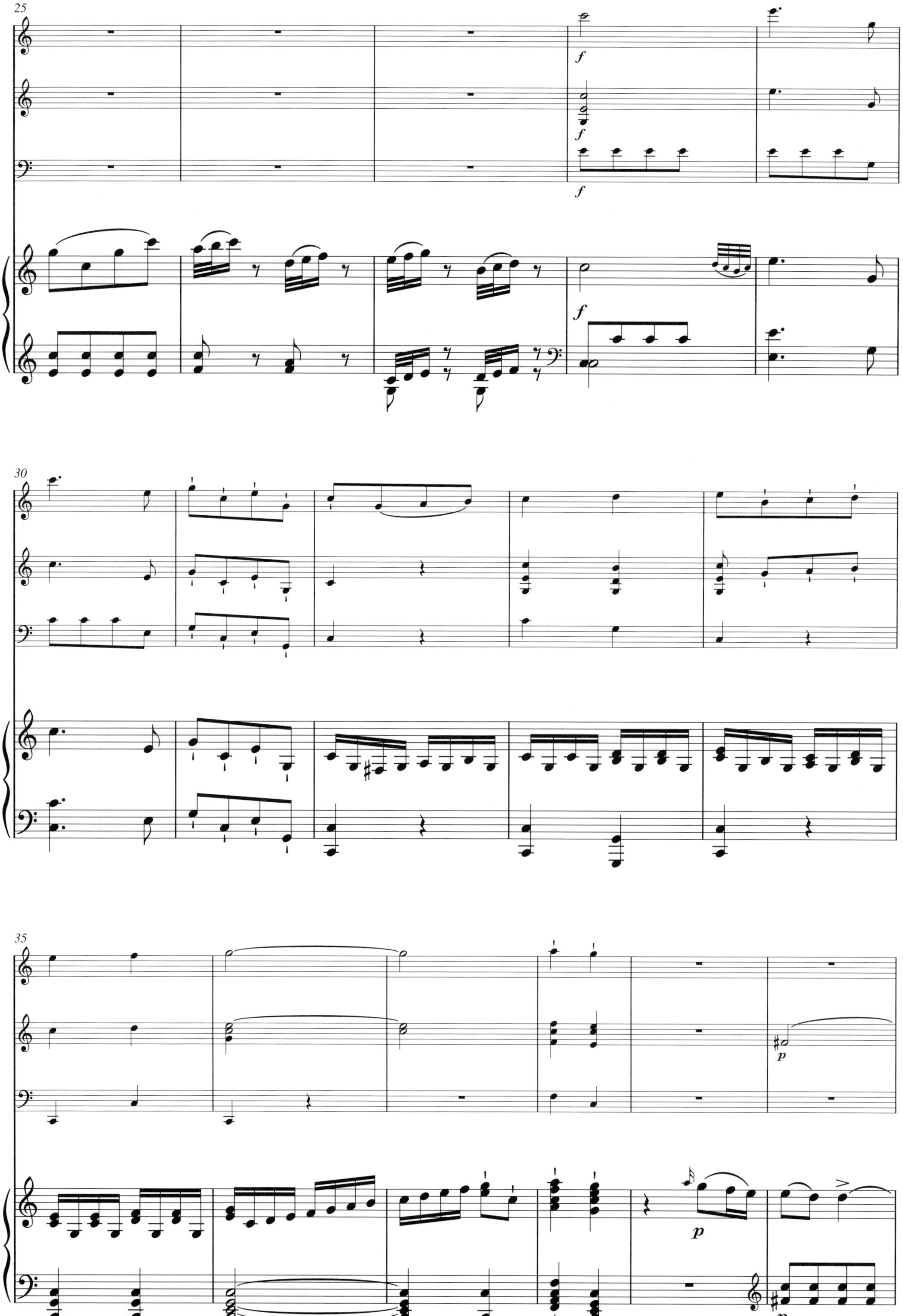
25
f
30
35
p

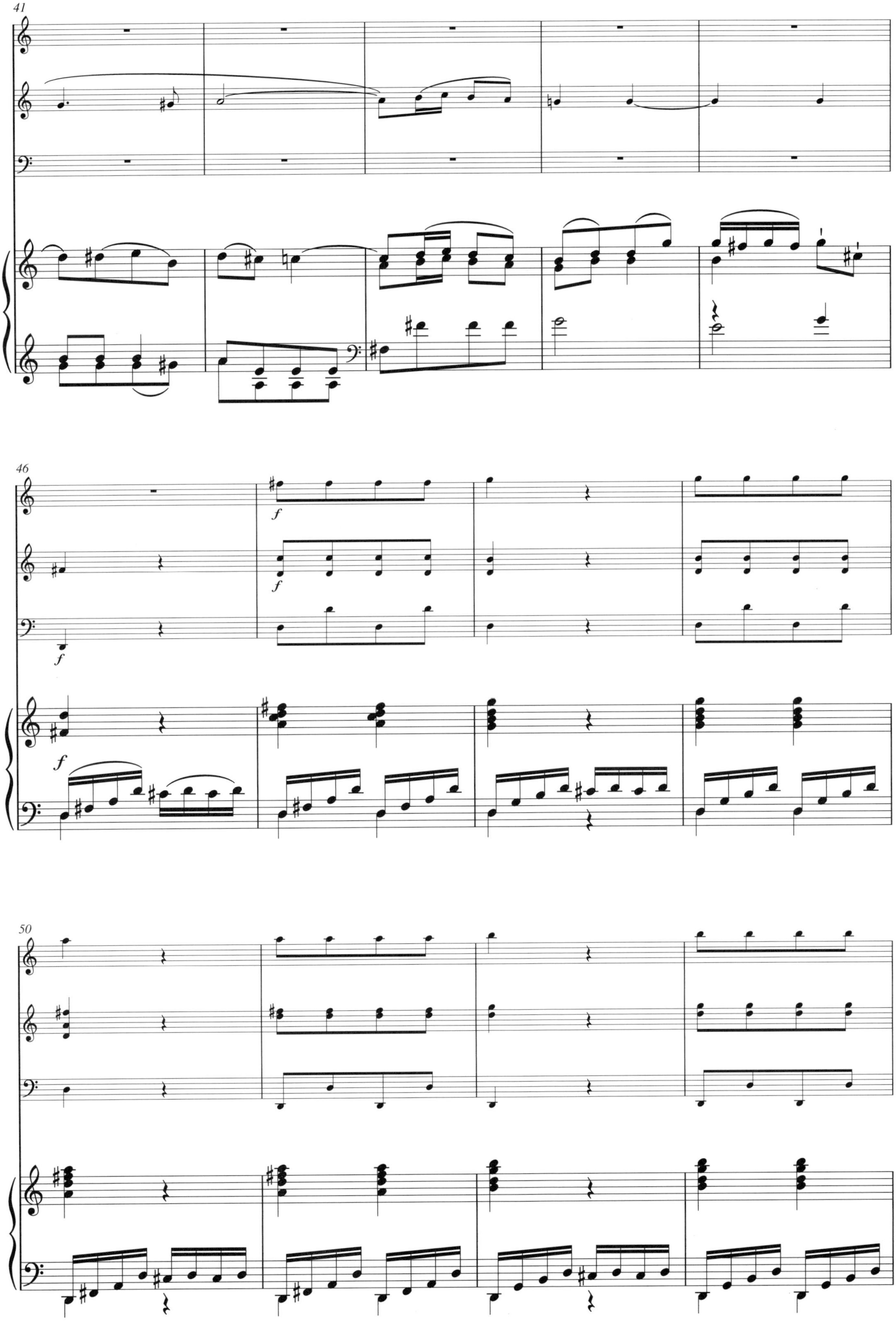
41
46
f
f
f
f
50

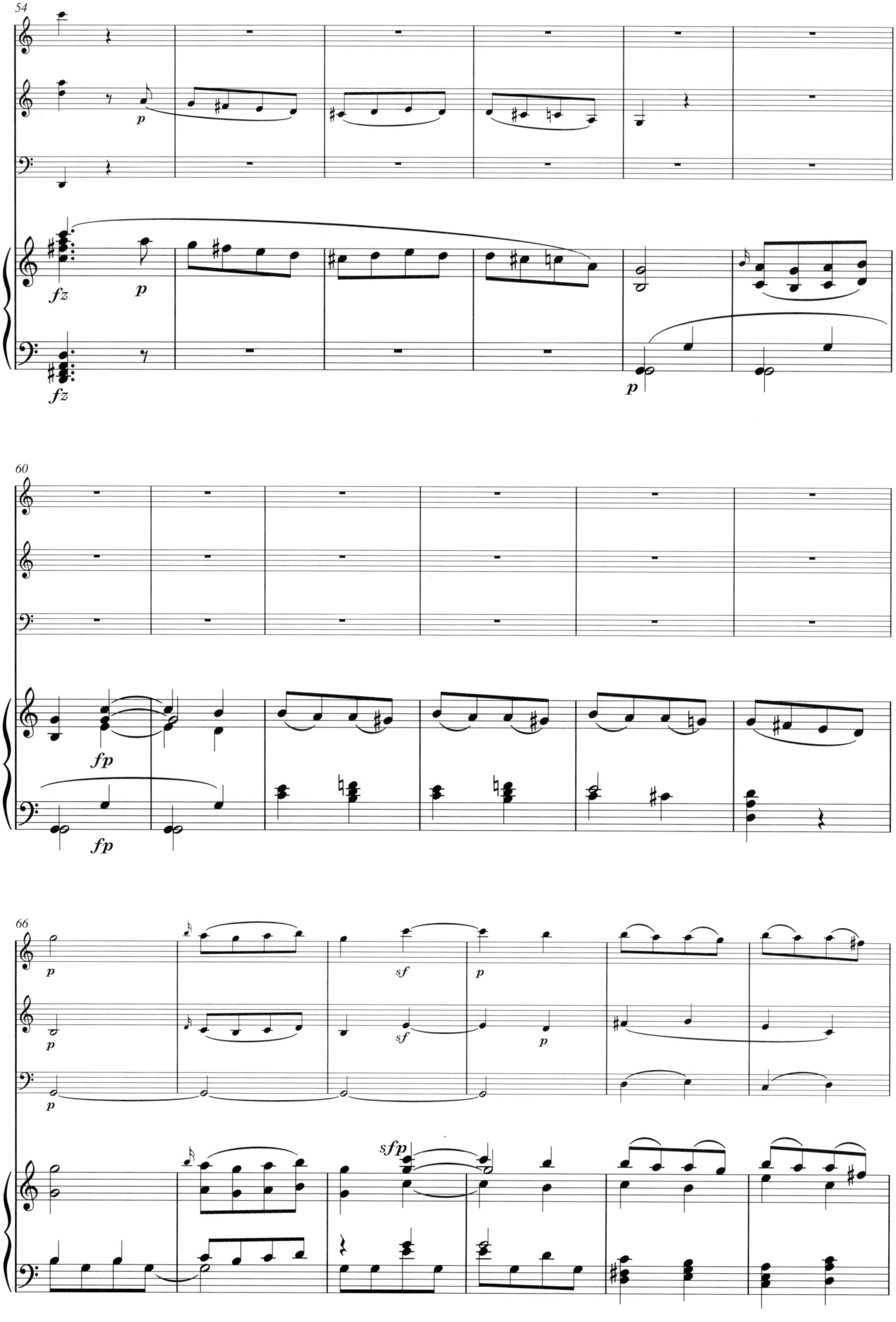
54
60
66

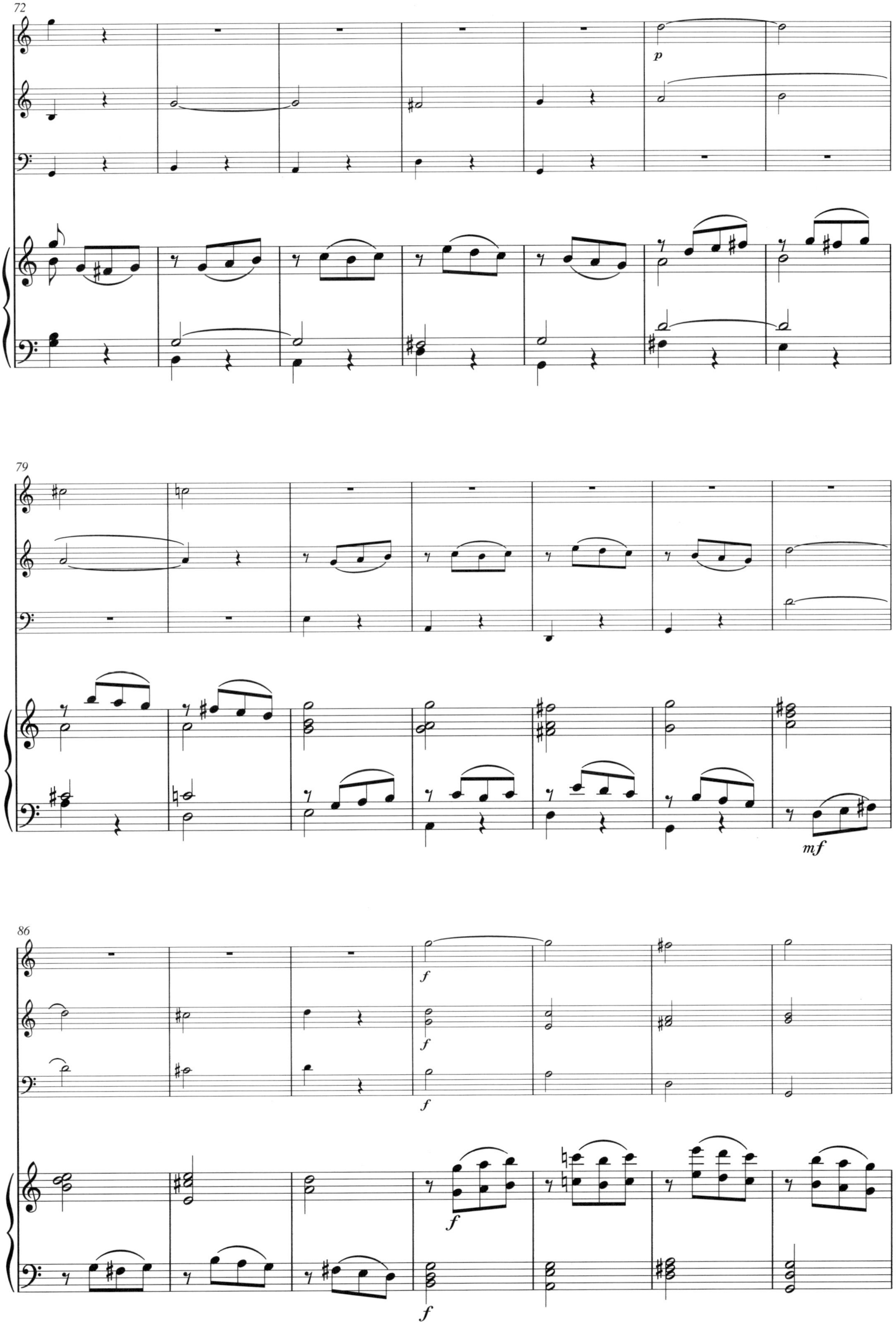
72
p
79
mf
86
f
f
f
f
f

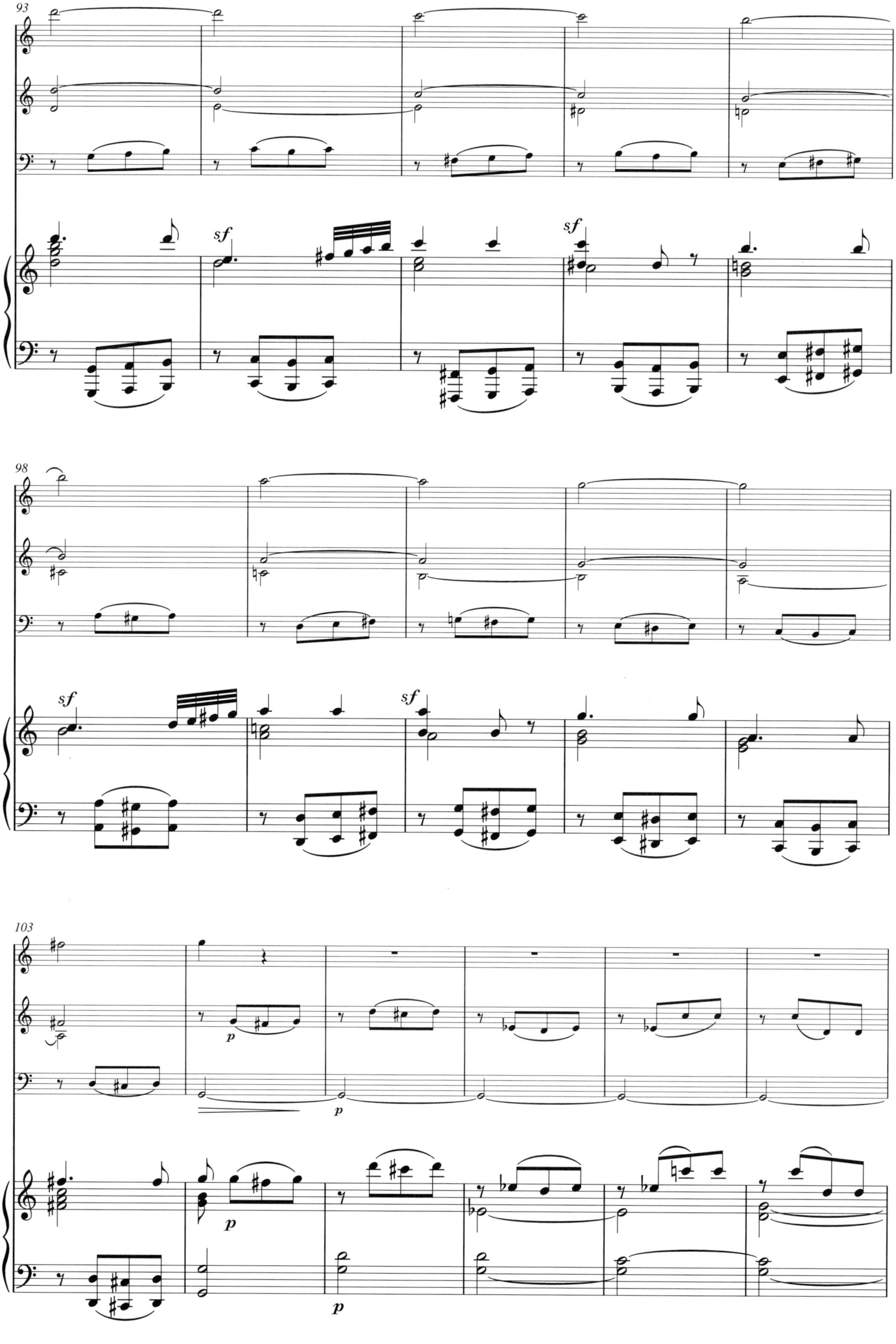

95

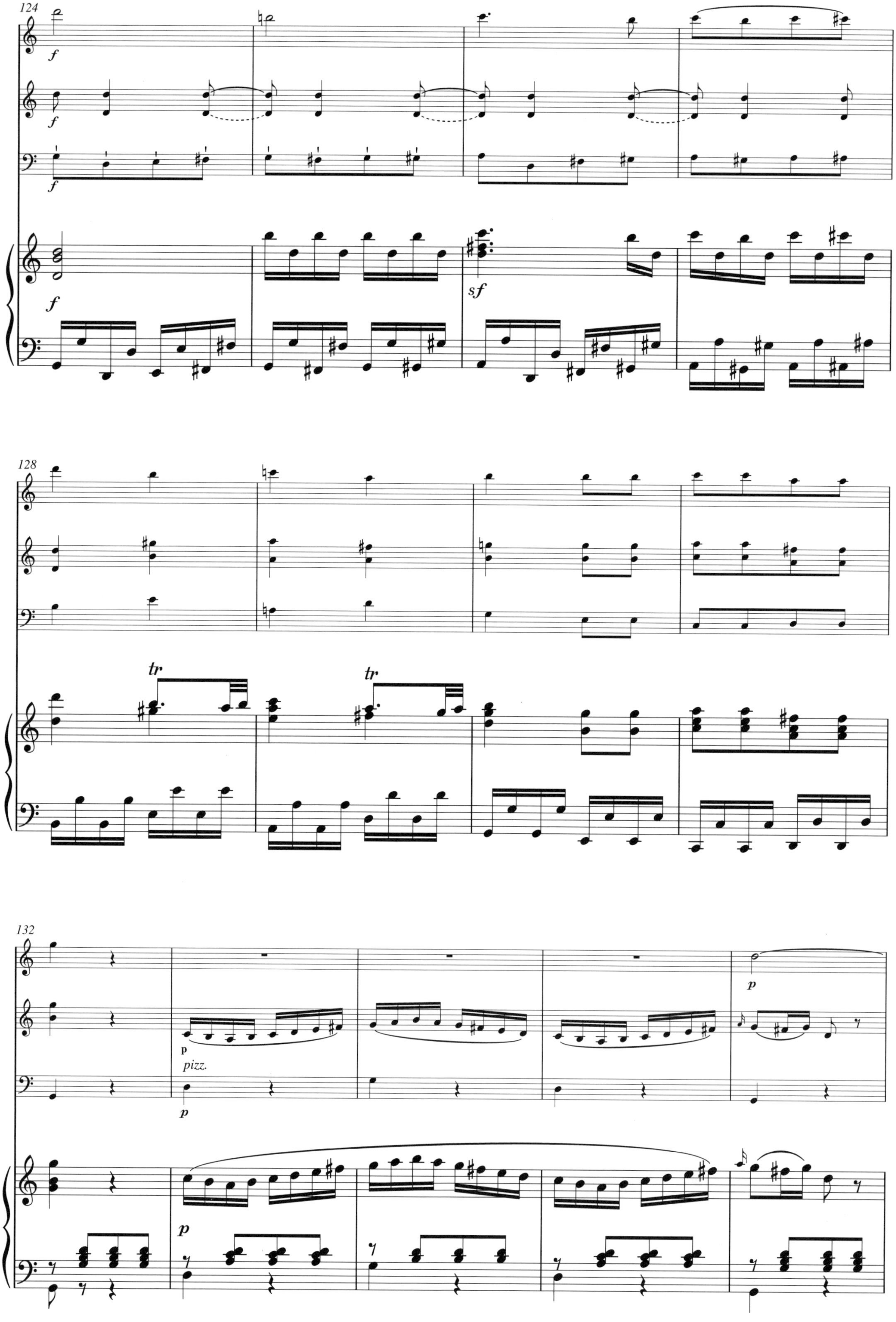
124
f
f
f
f
sf
128
tr
tr
132
p
pizz.
p
p
p

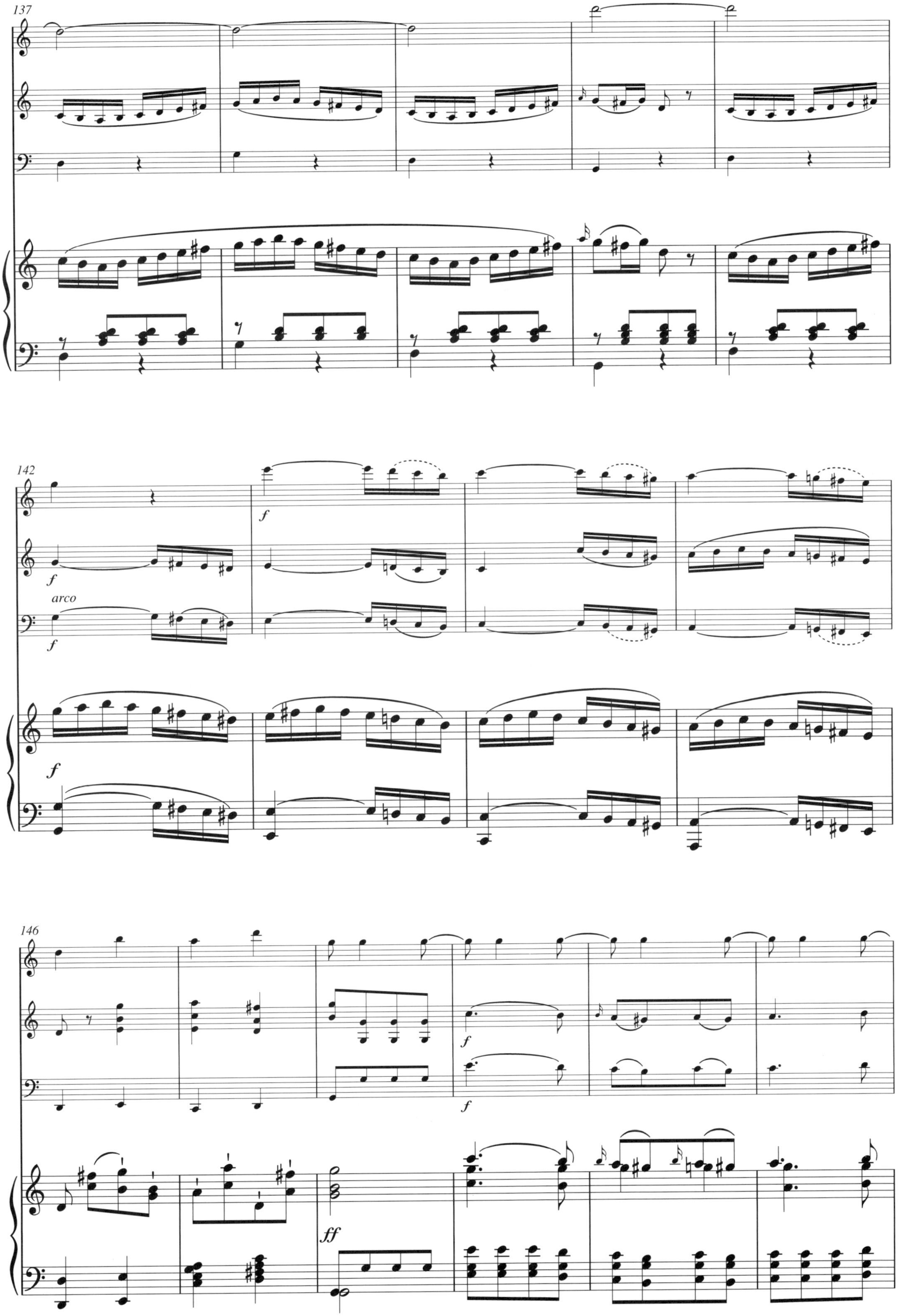
137
142
f
arco
f
f
f
146
f
f
ff

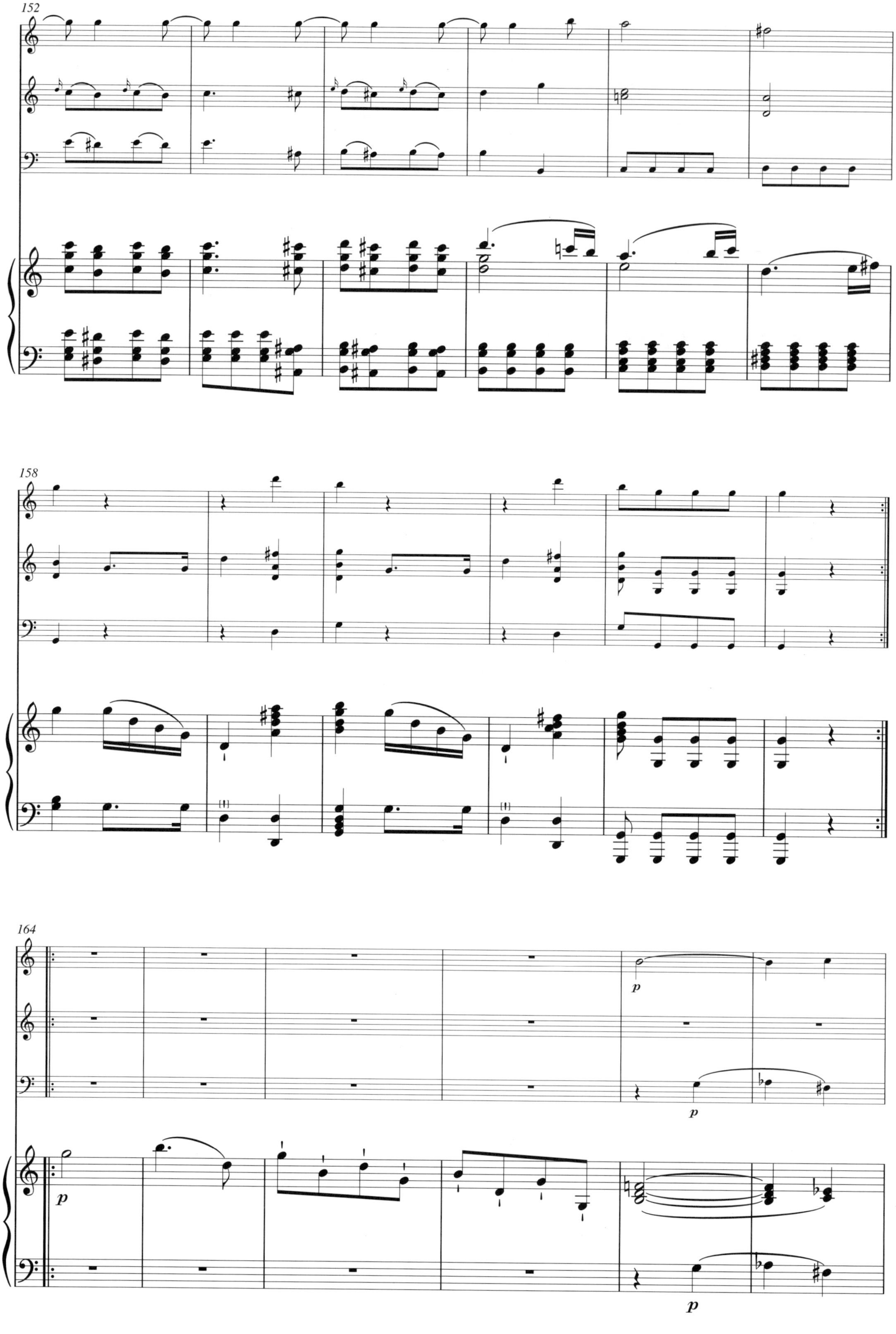
152
158
164
p
p
p
p

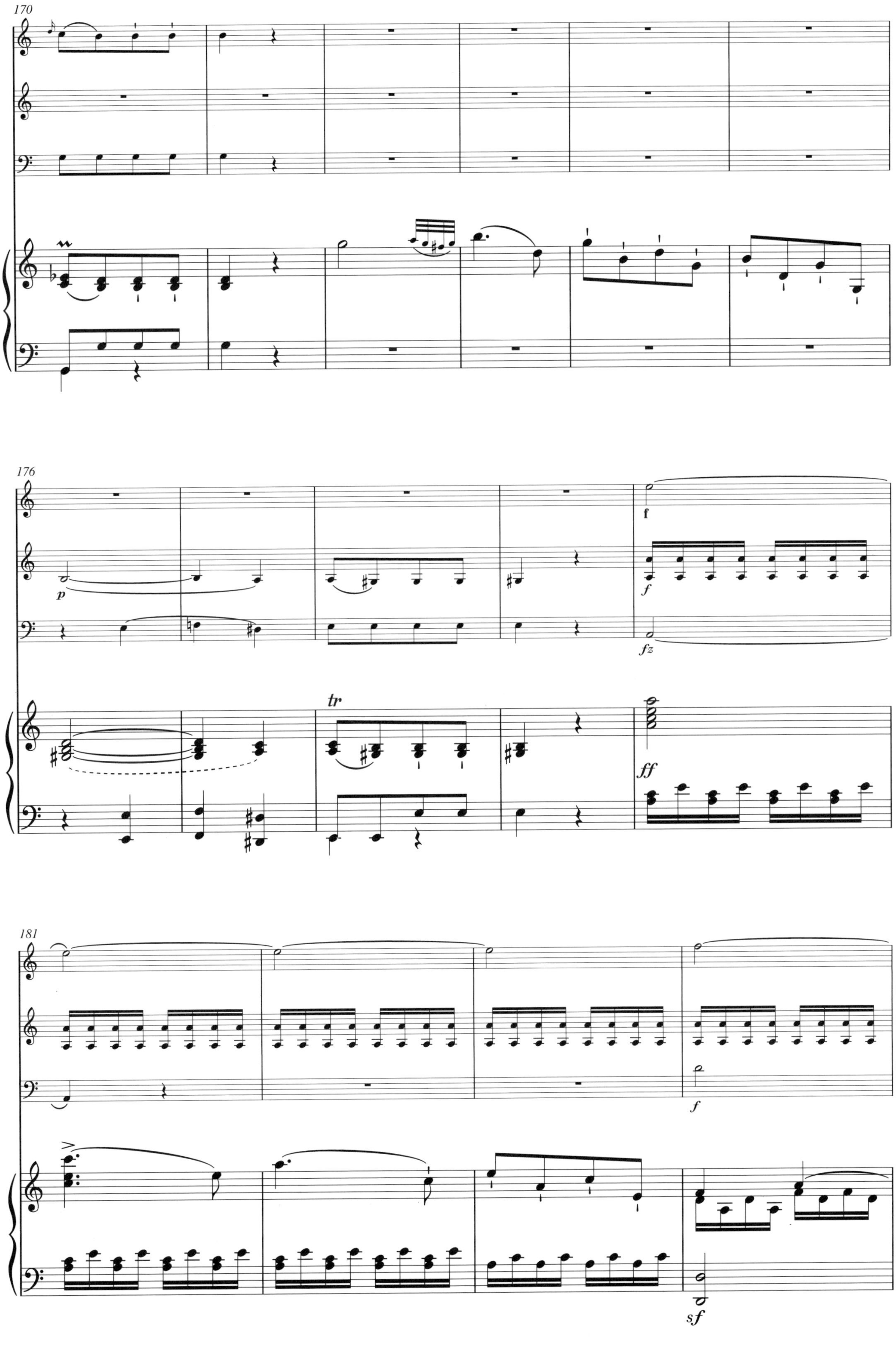
170
176
p
tr
f
f
fz
ff
181
f
sf

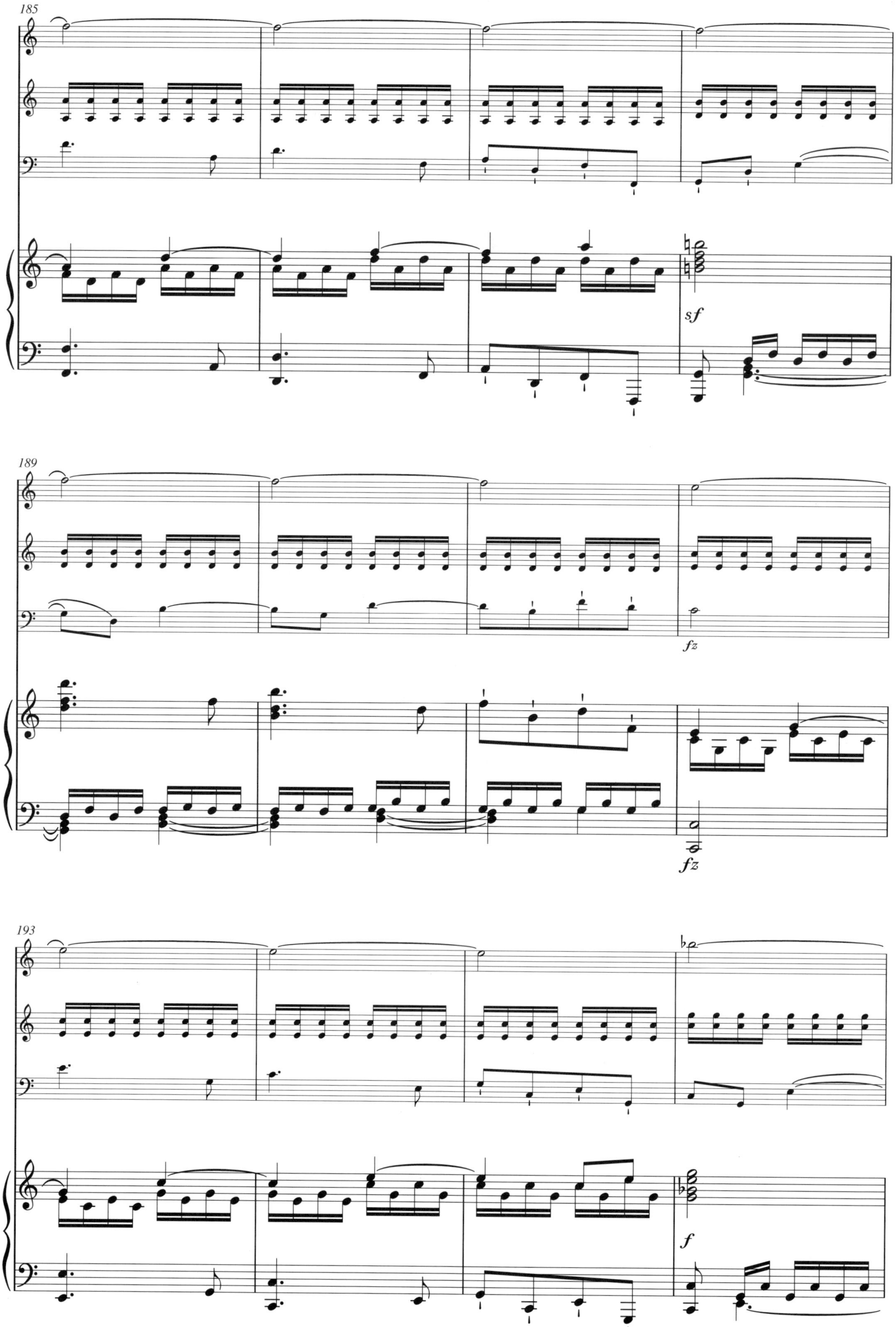
185
sf
189
fz
fz
193
f

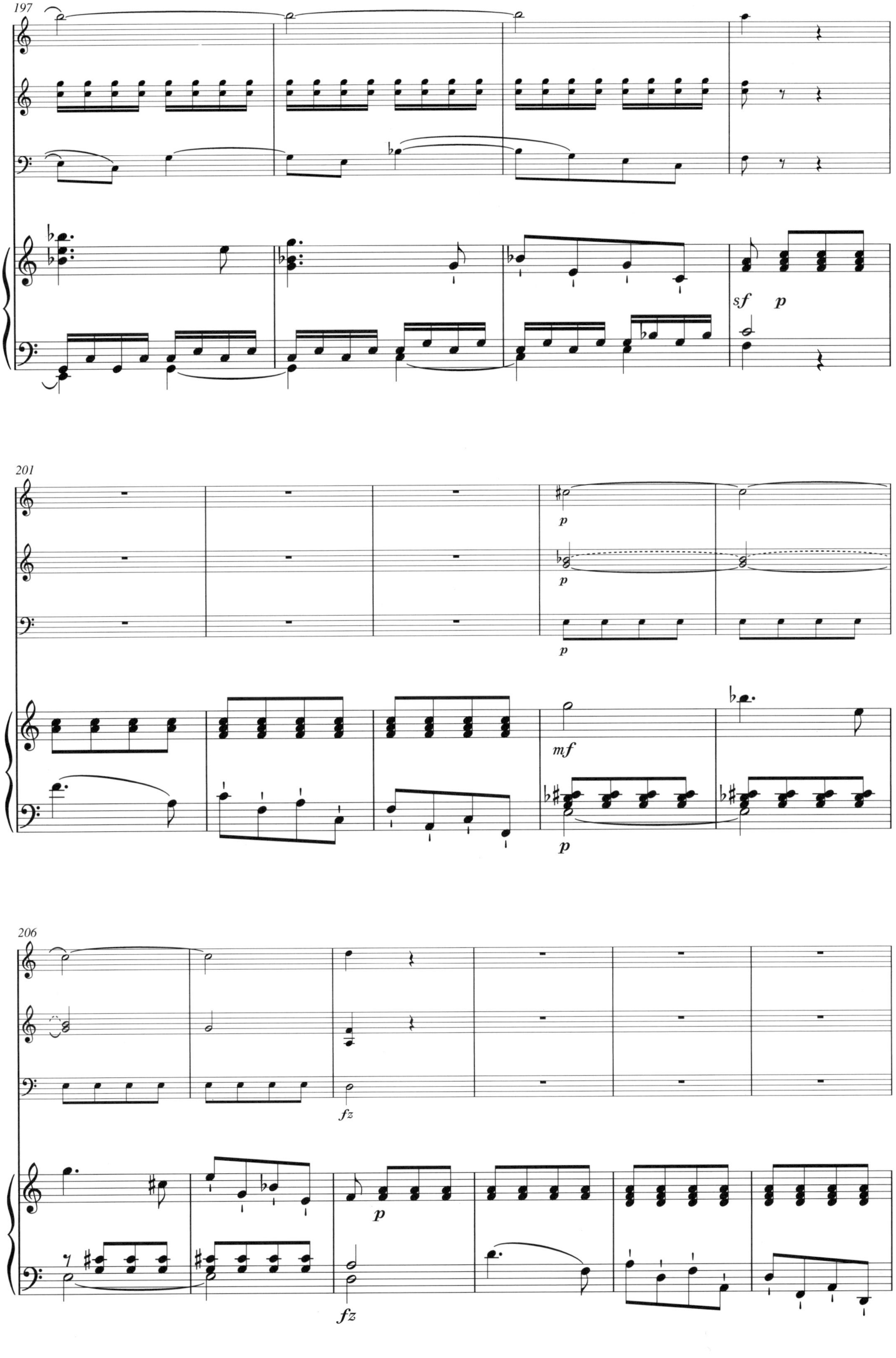
197
sf p
201
p
p
p
mf
p
206
fz
fz
p

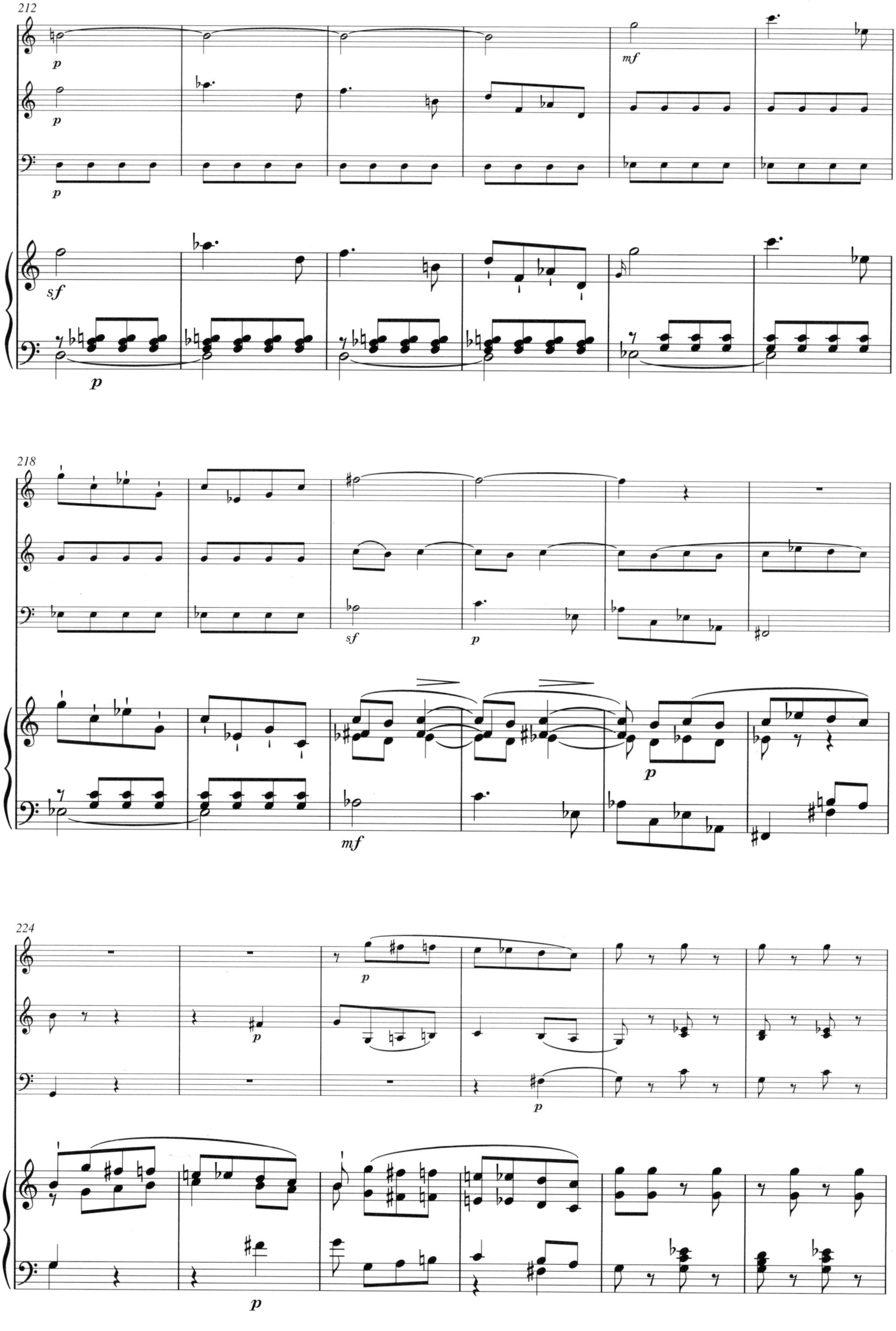
212
218
224

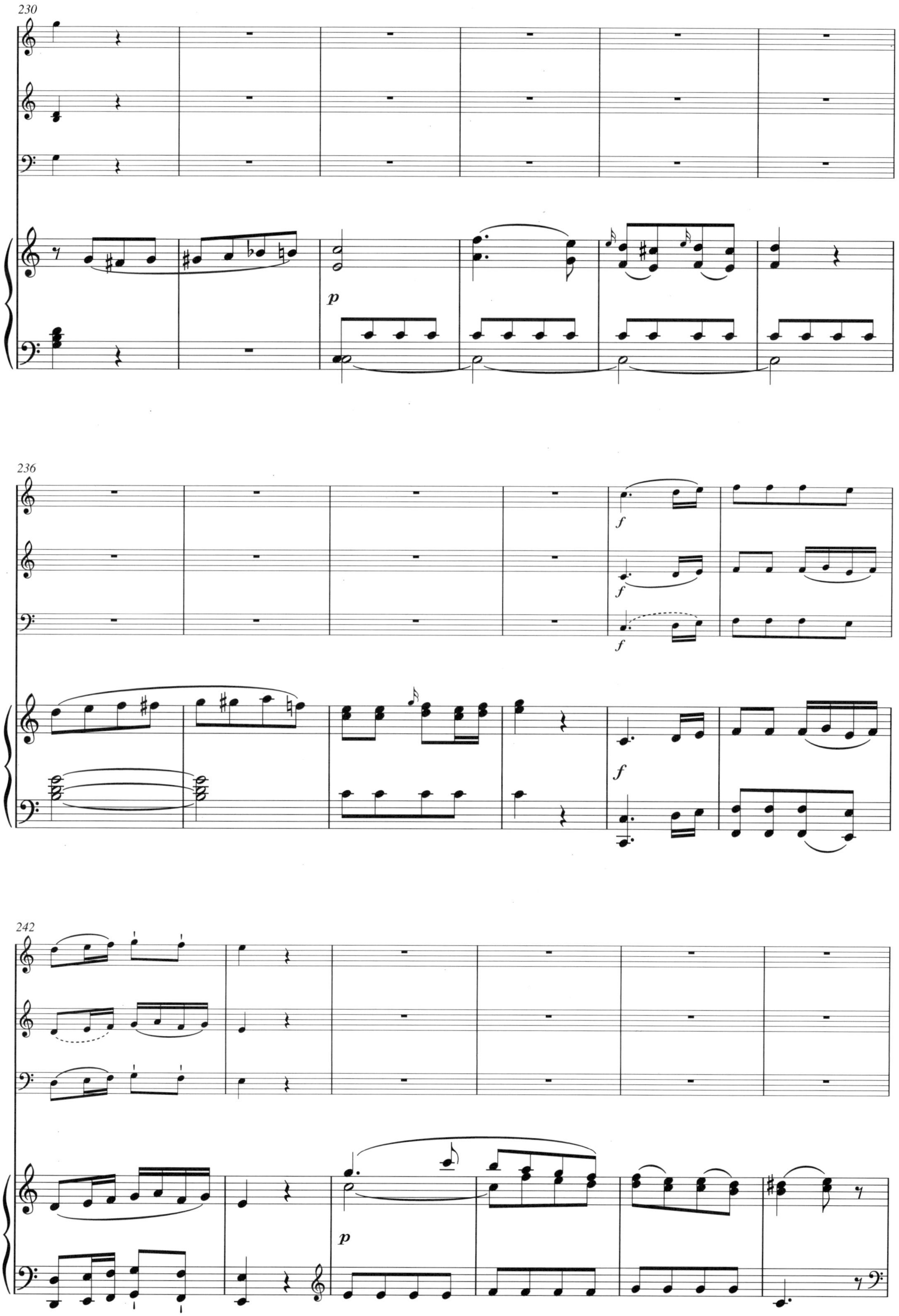
230
p
236
f
f
f
f
242
p

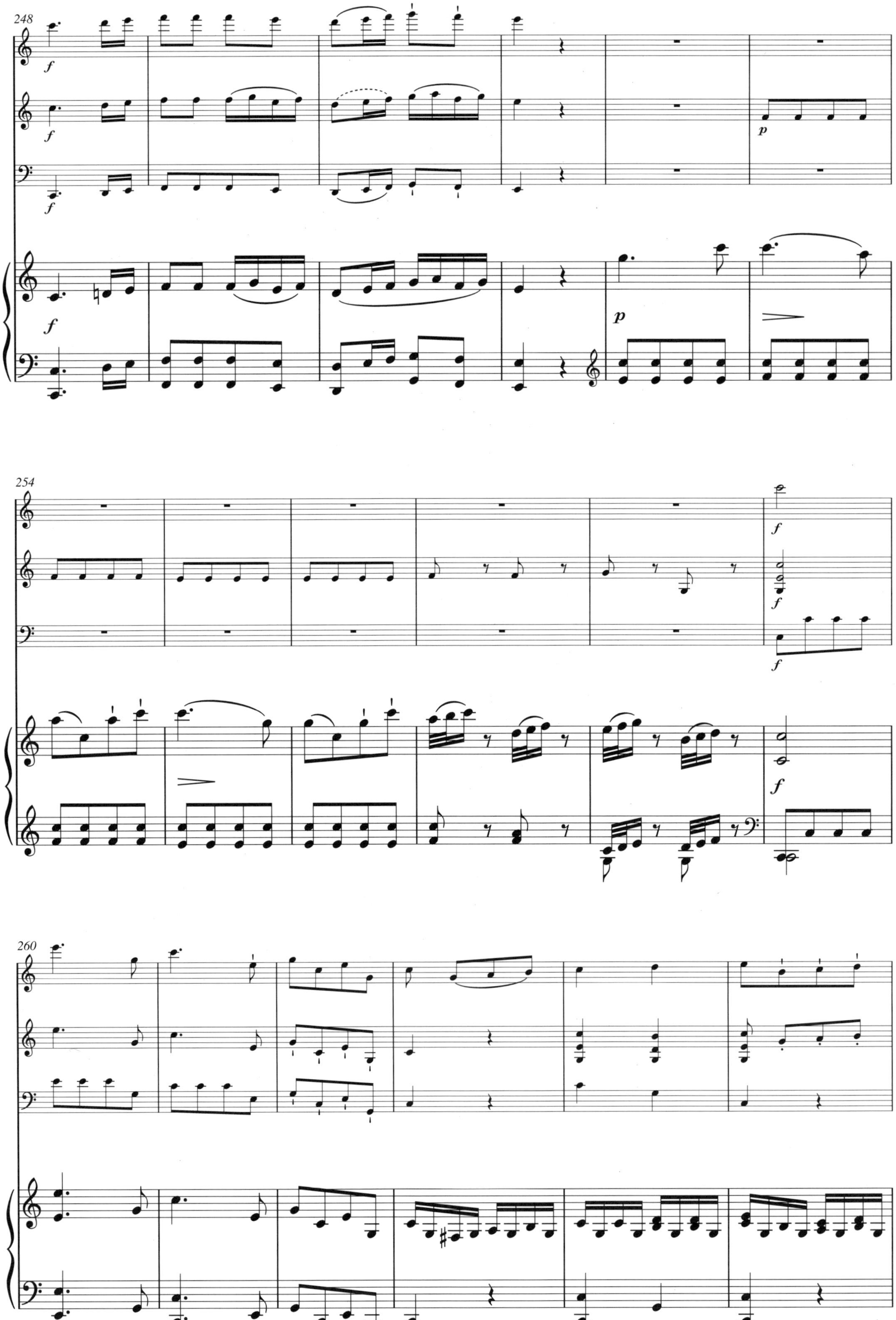
248
254
260

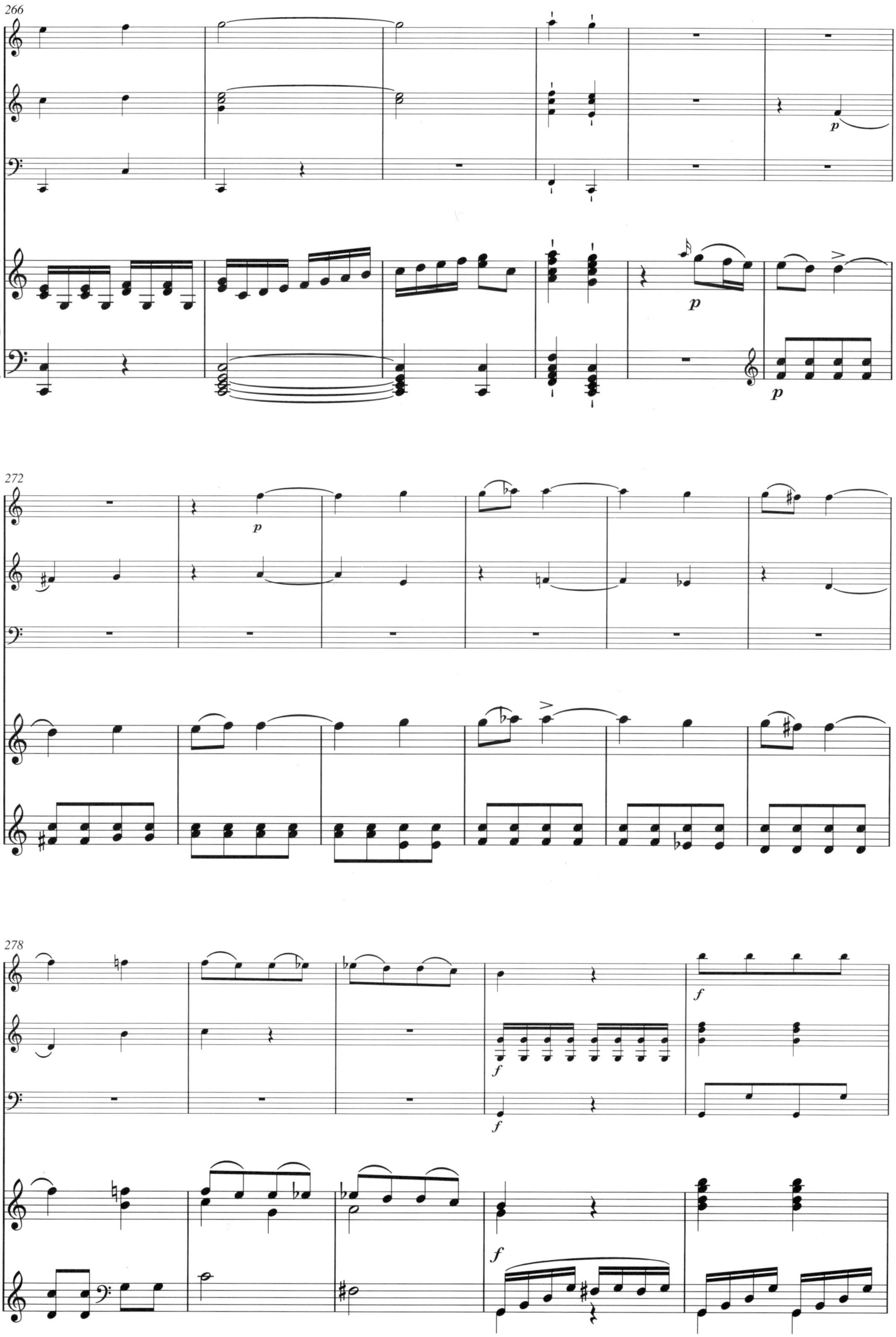
266
p
p
p
272
p
278
f
f
f
f

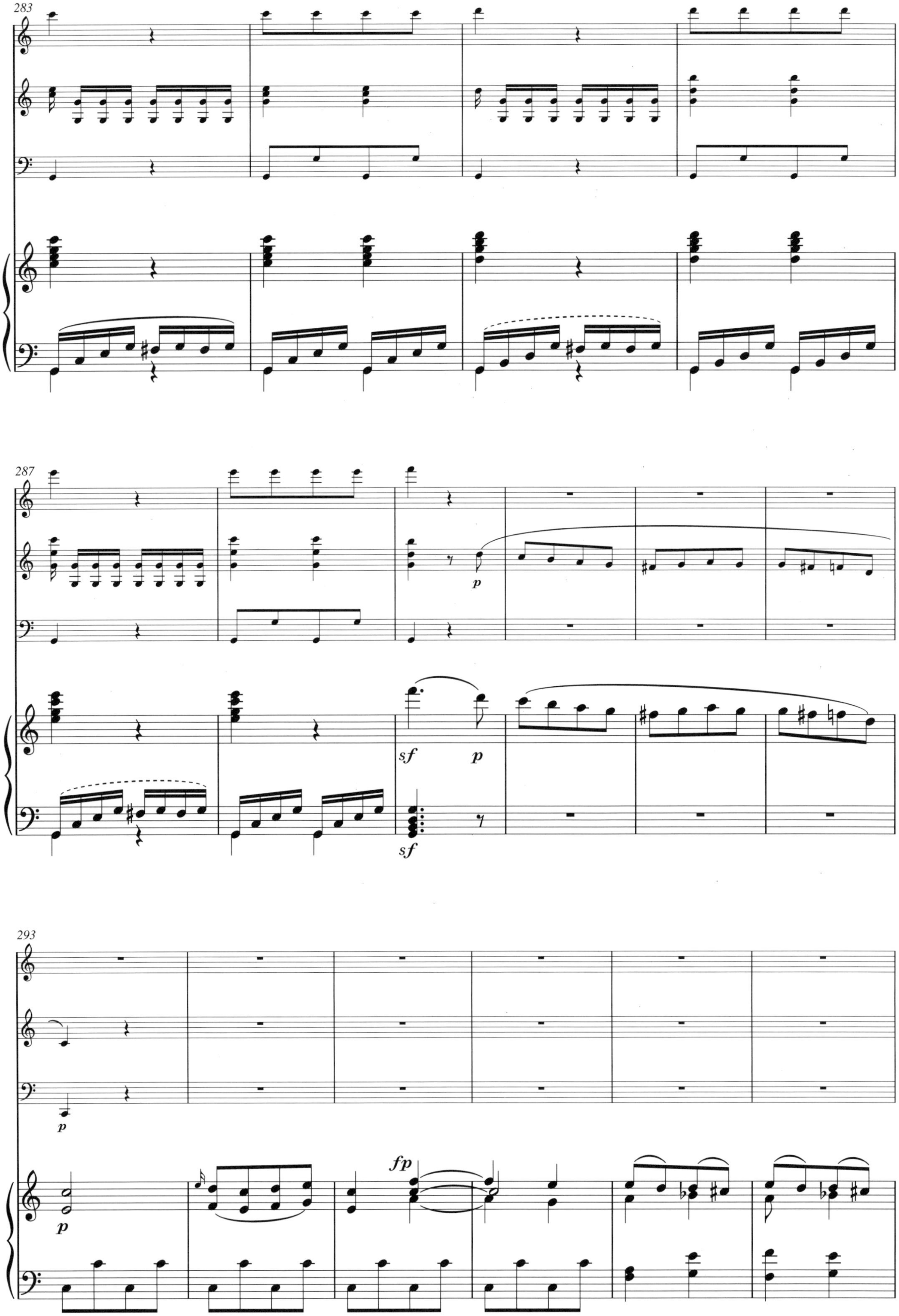
283
287
p
sf
p
sf
293
p
p
fp
p

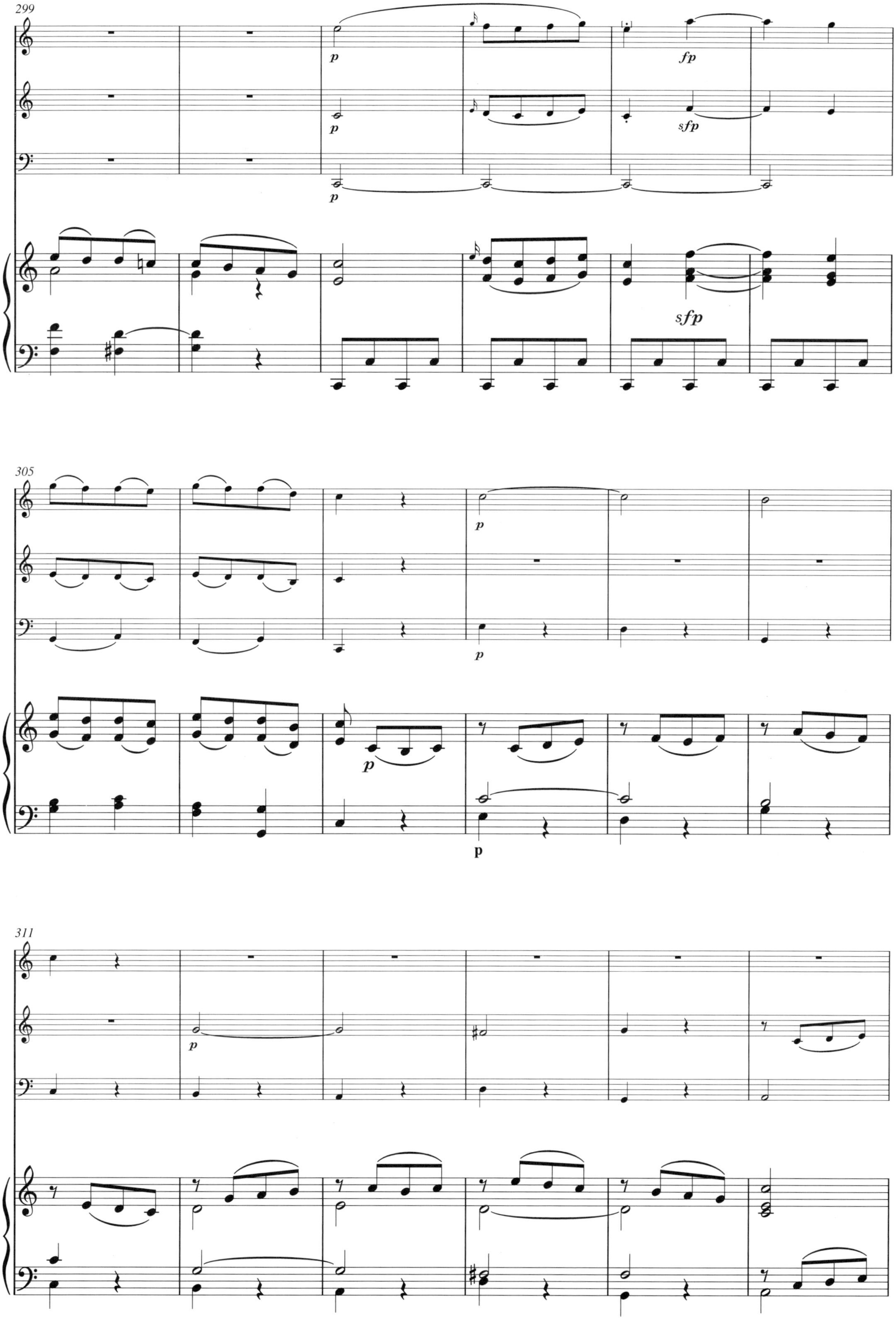
299
p
fp
sfp
305
p
311

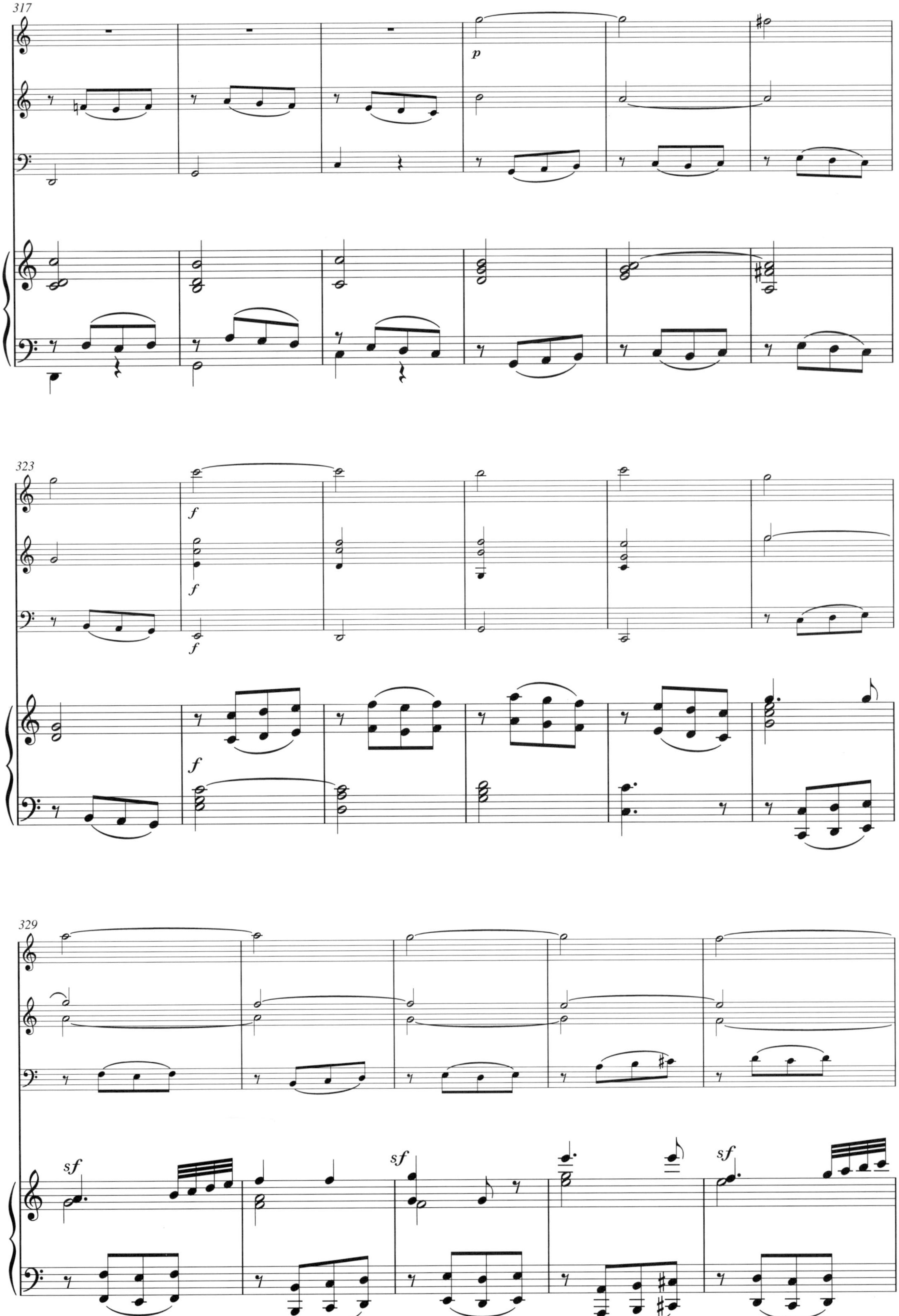
317
323
329

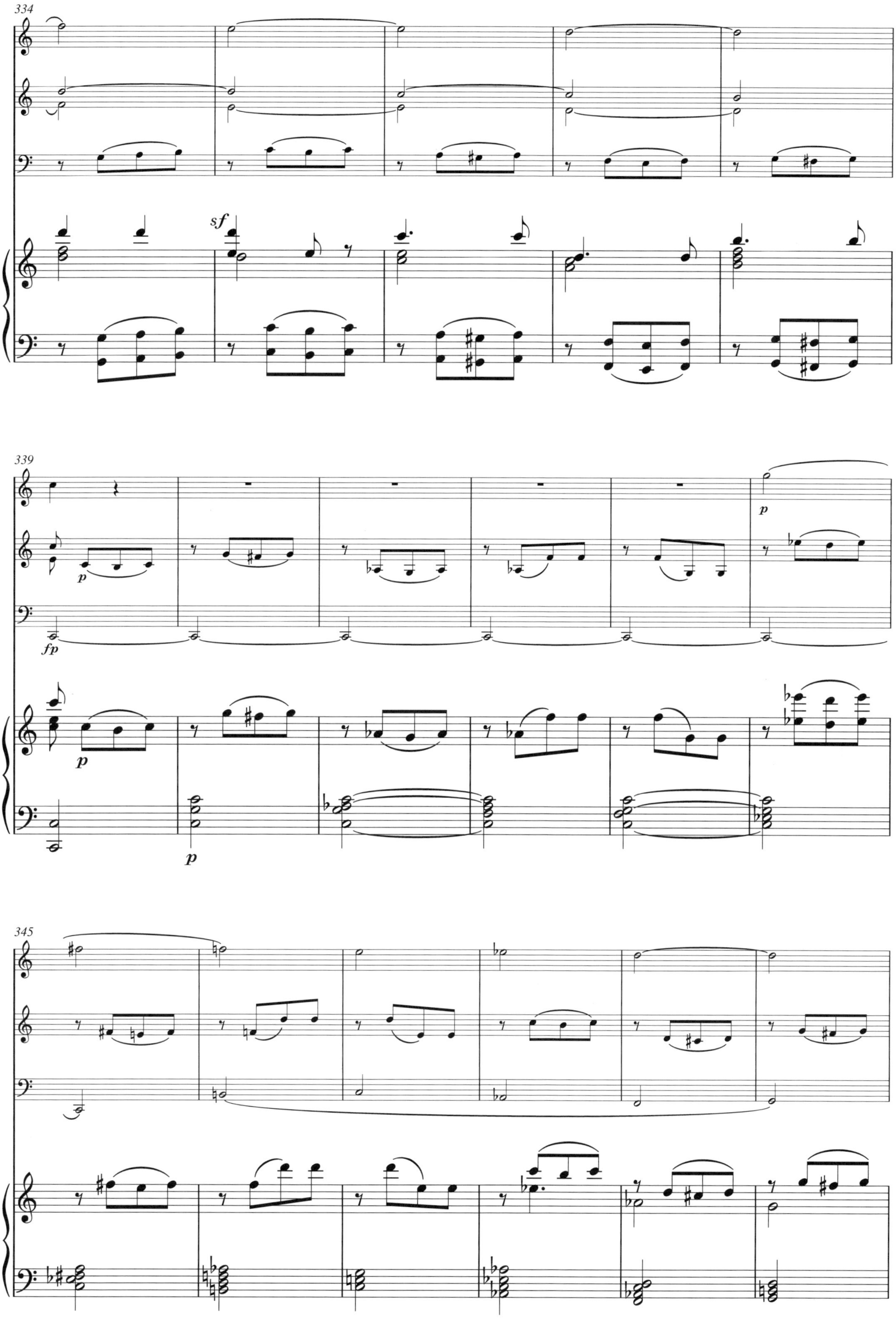
334
sf
339
p
fp
p
p
345

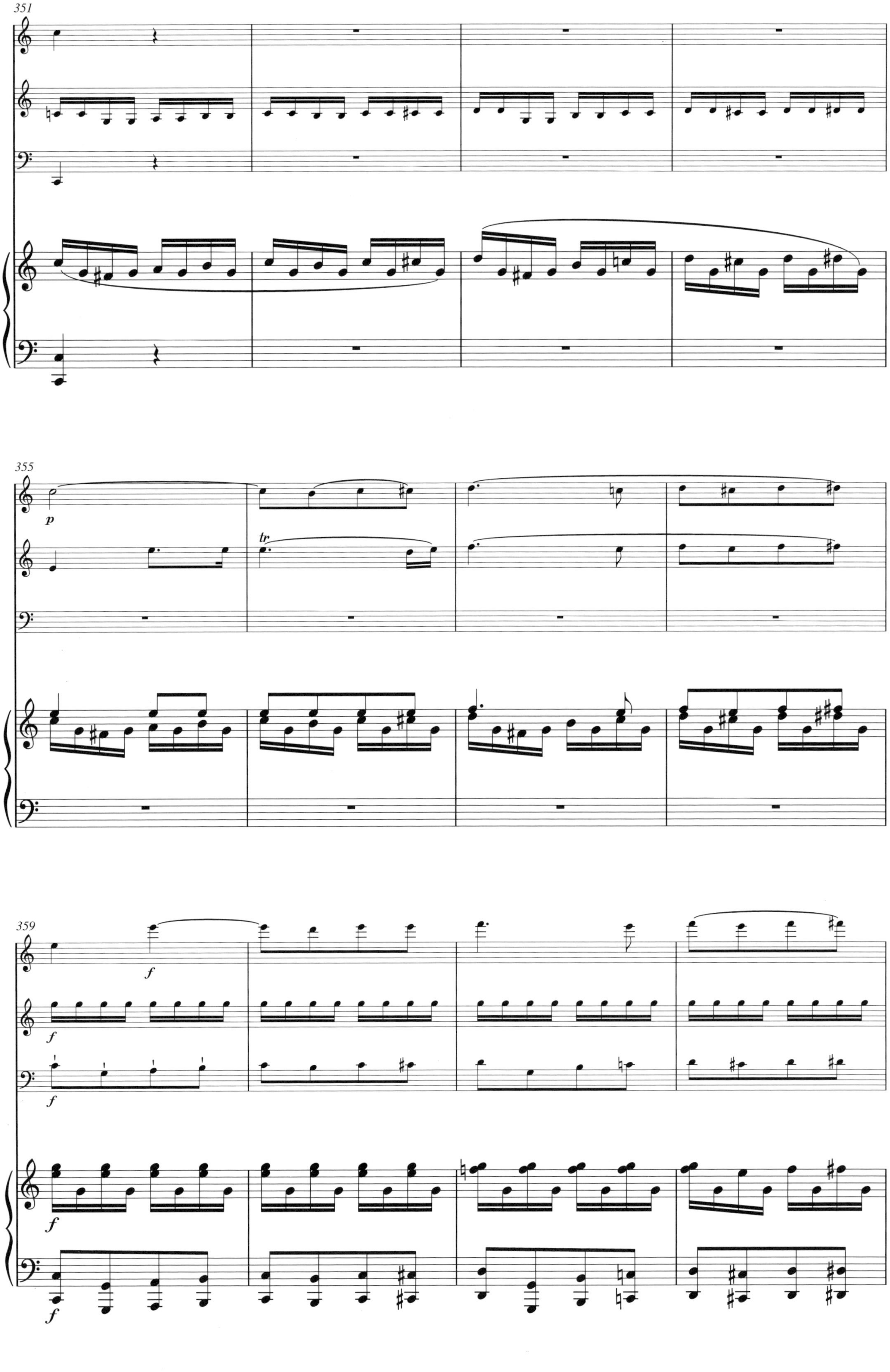
351
355
359

111

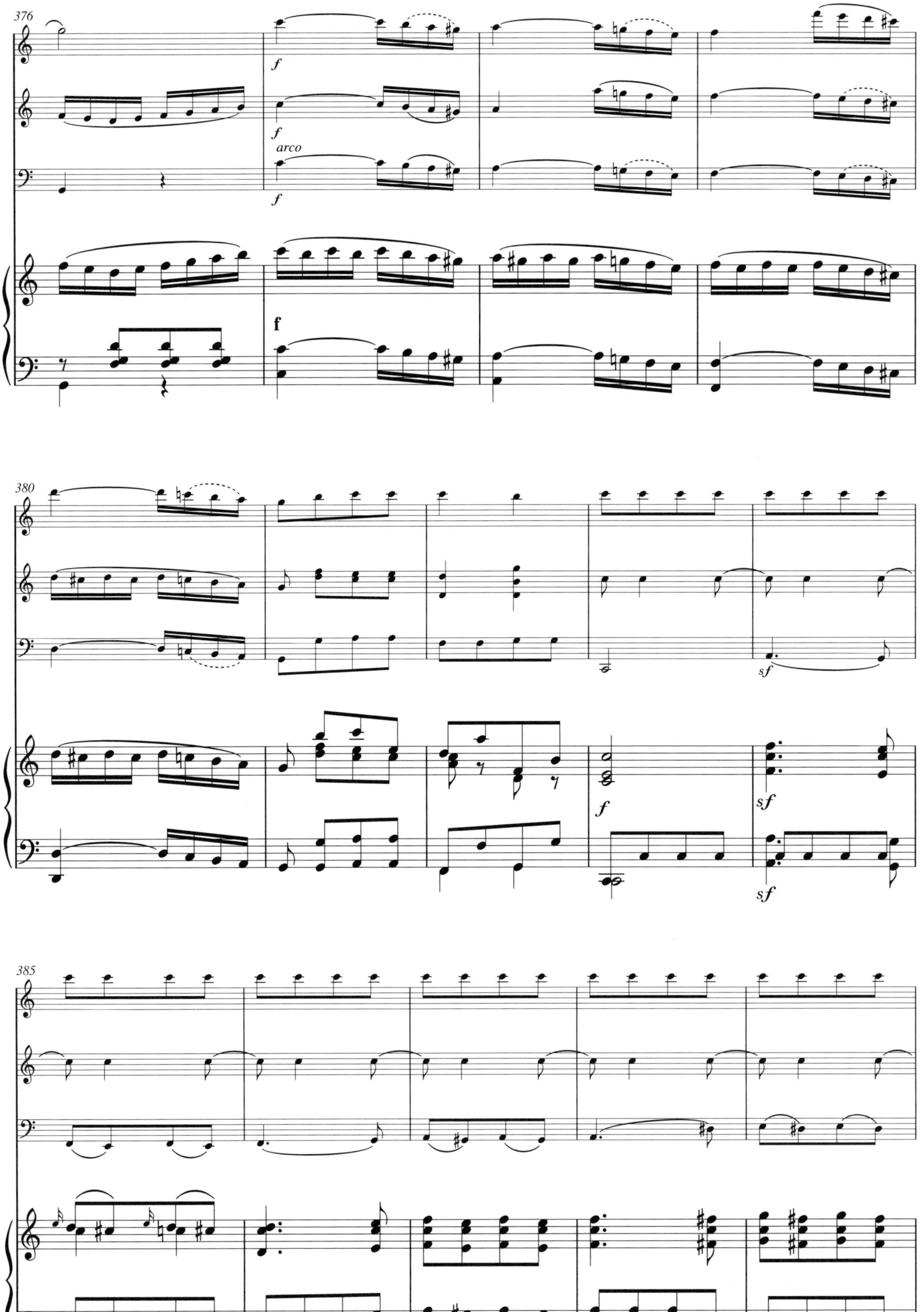
376
f
f
arco
f
f
380
sf
f
sf
sf
385

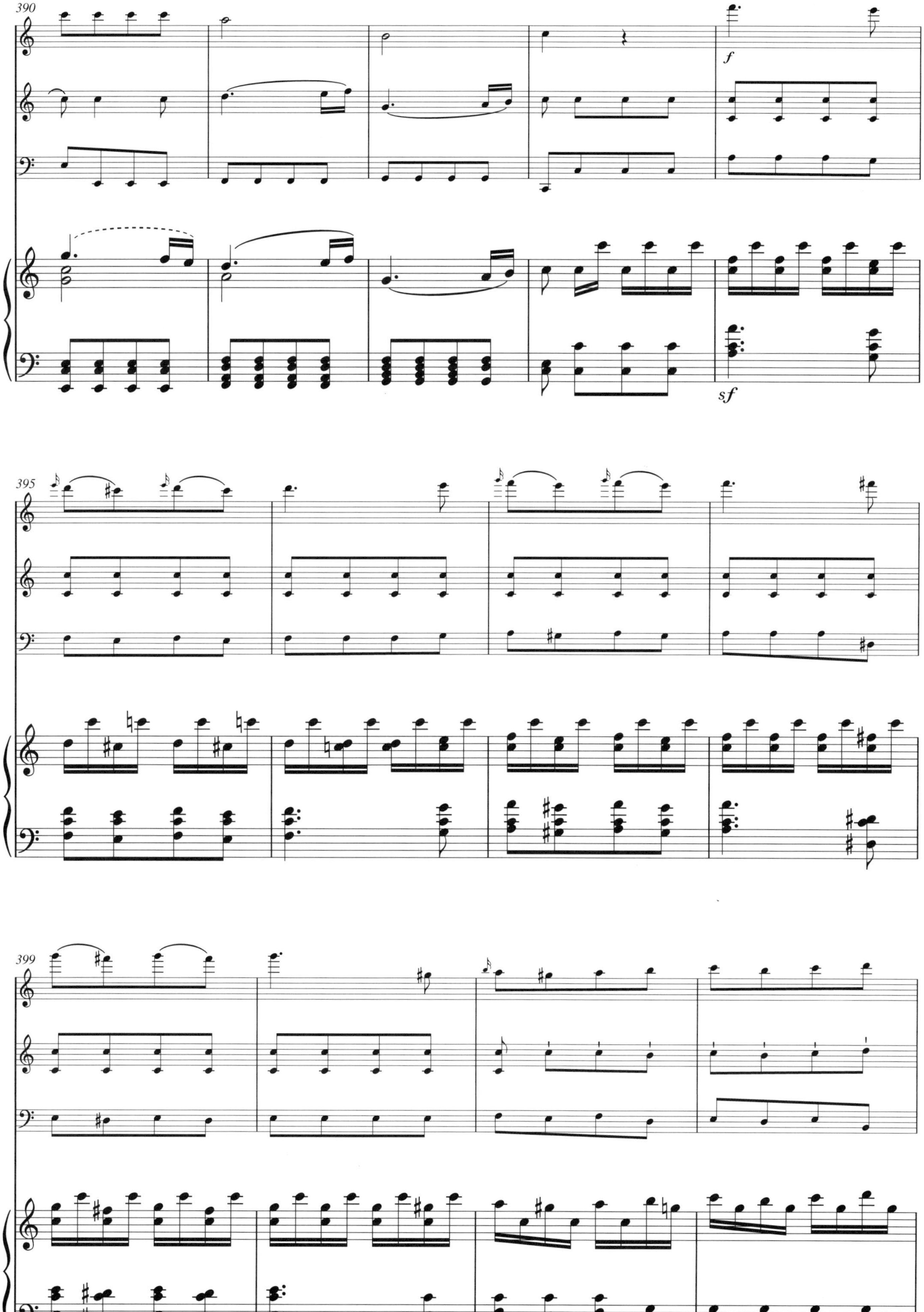
390
f
sf
395
399

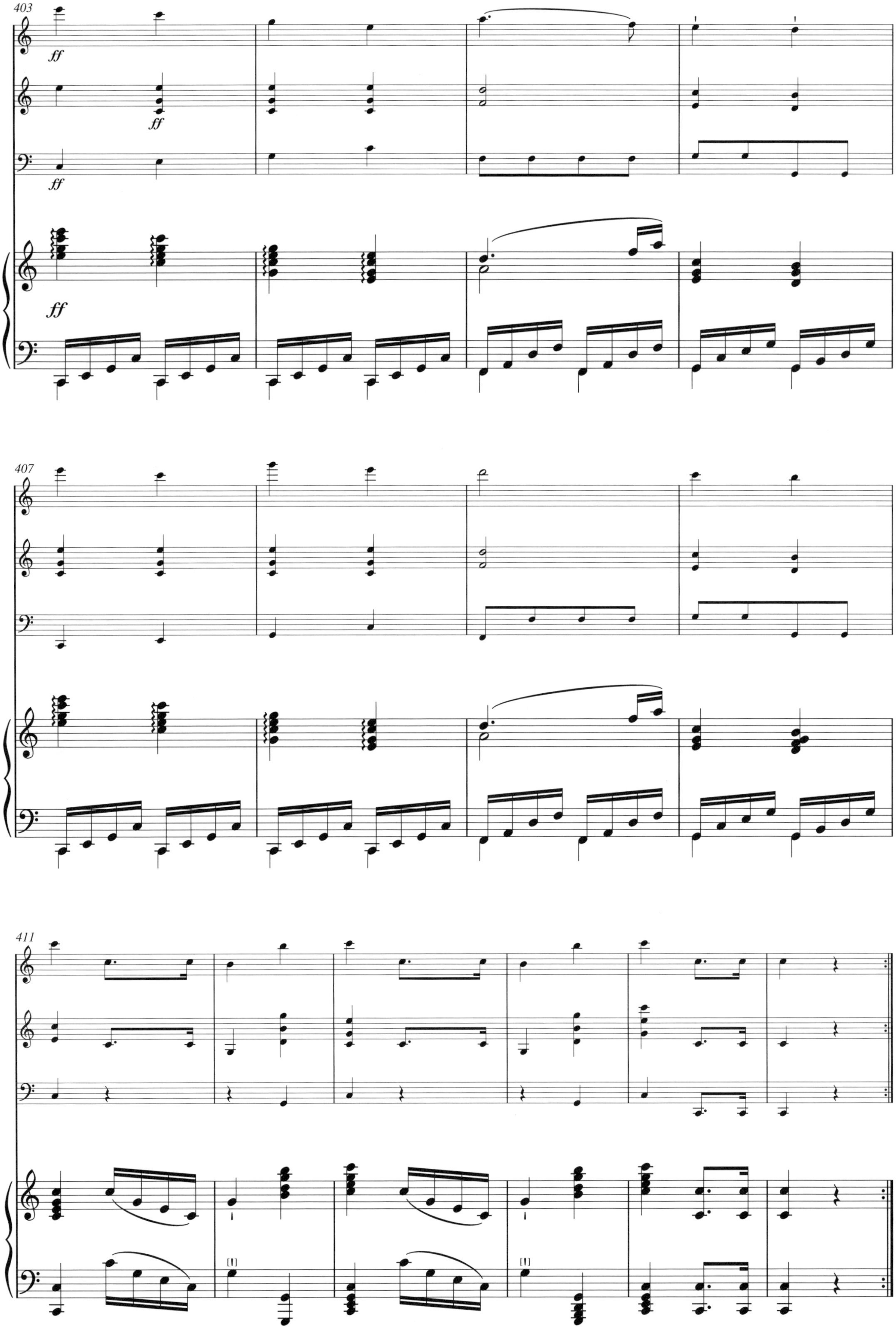
403
ff
ff
ff
ff
407
411
[!]
[!]

Critical Report

Sources

The two major sources of the arrangements are English (Chappell) and German (Schott). Each collection contains arrangements for an ensemble of flute, violin, cello, and pianoforte of six Mozart symphonies: K. 504, 550, 543, 425, 385, and 551.

The English edition was published by Chappell and was entered into Stationer's Hall on 10 August 1824. The title reads:

> Mozart's | Six | Grand Symphonies, | Arranged for the | Piano Forte. | with Accompaniments of | Flute Violin & Violoncello, | by | J. N. Hummel. | Maitre de Chapelle to the | Duke of Saxe Weimar. | No. 6 | London | Printed & Sold for the Proprietor, | by Chappell & Co. 50, New Bond Street and | to be had of all the principal Music Shops.

(British Library, H 408)

The German edition was published by Schott. Its title is:

> Grande Sinfonie | No. I | composé par | W. A. Mozart, | arrangé | Pour le Pianoforte | avec accompagnement | de Flute, Violon et Violoncello | et dédiée | à Son Excellence | Monsieur de e Goethe | Ministre d'Etat de S. A. R. le Grand-Duc de Saxe-Weimar | par | J. N. HUMMEL. | Propriété des Editeurs | Leipsic | chez Breitkopf & Härtel. | Pr. 2 Rthlr.

(Staatsbibliothek Marburg, D. Ms. 56 104)

The Schott probably appeared in 1823, but it is not possible to ascertain this with complete accuracy. Hummel had written to Peters on 29 November 1823 that "Härtel sent to me only a copy of each of the Mozart symphonies which I had arranged for Schultz, one of which was dedicated to the Royal Princess and the other to Goethe,"[1] and it is possible that he was referring to the symphonies K. 385 and K. 425. Moreover, this is the same letter in which he referred to both Schott and Simrock as "note-thieves."[2] Simrock had obviously published (and stolen?) his own edition of these works at approximately the same time. Other than a new title page, Simrock's publication is identical to the Schott in every detail, including the curious fact that they both use the same engraver's plate number of 2073. The format is also the same, in which the piano part is published in horizontal format and the instrumental parts in vertical format. This situation most probably represents another example of publishing piracy, as discussed previously, or perhaps an instance in which Hummel was following his habit of offering his works to several publishers at the same time.

Editions of Hummel's transcriptions of Mozart's symphonies were published in subsequent years by a number of firms, but primarily in solo piano version. As we discussed, these were clearly more marketable. For example, the symphonies were published by Schott in Paris in 1825, with the addition of the Symphony K. 543, as *6 Grande sinfonies*, but this version was "pour le piano."

When we turn to the English Chappell edition of 1824, numerous factors establish solid ground to assume that this represents the most accurate text of Hummel's work, and the first publication. We must remember that all of Hummel's arrangements were commissioned for England by Schultz, published there probably under his supervision, and many were indeed deposited at Stationer's Hall. The deposit records can therefore be used to ascertain a reasonably close date of publication or composition. For further confirmation, the first page of both the violin and the cello parts in the Schott carries the inscription, in English, "Mozart's Symphony No. 5 arranged by Hummel." This is identical to the Chappell designation and could only have come from copying the original and earlier English edition. The English publication is therefore the primary source used for this edition.

Editorial Methods

Both the Chappell and Schott editions are, on the whole, clear and unambiguous with regard to text and performance indications. There is no full score, but only a piano part and separate parts for the other three instruments. In the present volume, editorially added elements are placed in brackets, except that added slurs and ties are dashed, and added letter dynamics are set in bold (rather than the customary bold-italic) type. General editorial policies are as follows. Roman numerals have been added at the beginnings of movements. The spelling and orthography of performance directives (such as *dolce*, *cresc.*, etc.) have been regularized. Common stemming has been utilized where appropriate. Indications of measured tremolo have been realized. Rests have been added in some instances to clarify voice-leadings, but unnecessary extra rests have been removed. Slurs have been drawn to enclose ties. Redundant accidentals (primarily on notes tied over barlines) have been removed. The original note values of appoggiaturas have been retained except where reported in the critical notes.

The metronome markings are by Hummel. They appear in the first three movements of the *Haffner* in the Chappell edition, but not the last. However, for guidance about the tempo of this final movement, I direct the reader to Mozart's letter to his father of 7 August 1782, in which he writes that it should be played "as fast as possible."[3] Metronome markings are indicated in all four movements of the *Linz* (Chappell). For the Schott edition, none appear in any of the movements of the *Haffner*, but in all movements of the *Linz*. All other performance indications, such as the use of both staccato dots and strokes for shortened notes, are retained as in the original.

There are numerous instances in the edition in which the phrasing, articulation, and dynamics differ in parallel passages, or between two or more instruments playing at the same time. To cite a few examples, in the *Haffner*, the violin dynamic in movement I, measure 27, beats 1 and 3 is *fp*, while those of the cello are *sf*, and the piano indication is *f*. The phrasing in movement I, measure 63, beats 1 and 2 of the cello and piano are different, even though both are playing the same notes. In movement II, measure 7, beat 1, the cello is articulated with dots while the piano left hand uses strokes. This conforms to the intentional avoidance of regularization, which is a characteristic of many works written before the twentieth century. These are reproduced as in the original. Still, it must be allowed that in some instances phrasing can and should be added judiciously where it is absent from the source, or where inconsistencies are clearly the result of copyist errors or omissions. Such editorial additions have been made in brackets for articulations and through the use of dashed slurs. Finally, there are no pedal indications in the source and none have been added, but this, of course, does not imply that the pedal should not be used. For a more complete discussion of these issues, the reader is directed to "Notes on Performance" above.

Critical Notes

The following notes document readings of Chappell (the primary source) and Schott (the secondary source) where they differ from the edition in ways not accounted for by general editorial policies. Mention of one source indicates that the edition follows the reading found in the other source. If neither source is mentioned the report applies to both. Instruments are abbreviated as follows: Fl. = Flute, Vn. = Violin, Vc. = Violoncello, Pn. = Piano, r.h. = right hand, l.h. = left hand. Notes are numbered consecutively within a measure; notes sounding simultaneously are numbered from bottom to top. Where appropriate, chords or beats are numbered rather than specific notes.

Symphony in D Major, K. 385 (Haffner)

I. Allegro con spirito

Mm. 3, 5, 17, 60, 62, 131, and 133, Fl., notes 1–2 have strokes in Schott. M. 94, Fl., notes 1–3 have strokes in Schott. M. 99, Pn., r.h., chords 1–2 lack strokes in Schott. Mm. 147 and 148, Vn., note 1 lacks stem. Mm. 180, 181, and 182, Pn., l.h., second rest consists of quarter and eighth rests.

II. Andante

Mm. 17–21, Pn., r.h., strokes in Schott. M. 33, Pn., r.h., notes 3–4 lack strokes in Schott. M. 51, Pn., r.h., beat 1 has *fp* in Schott. Mm. 67 and 69, Pn., r.h., notes 4–5 and 11–12 have strokes in Schott. Mm. 68 and 70, Pn., r.h., chords 3–4 and 11–12 have strokes in Schott. Mm. 69–70, Fl., strokes are missing in Schott.

III. Minuetto

No notes.

IV. Finale: Presto

M. 129, Pn., l.h., chord 2 lacks stroke in Schott. M. 130, Pn., l.h., chord lacks stroke in Schott. Mm. 212, 213, and 214, Pn., beat 2 has *fp* in Schott.

Symphony in C Major, K. 425 (Linz)

I. Adagio; Allegro spiritoso

M. 13, Vn., note has *p*. M. 20 lacks repeat bar. M. 42, Vn., note 1 lacks stem. M. 54, Vn., notes 1–2 lack strokes in Schott. Mm. 66 and 67, Vc., beat 2 has crescendo hairpin in Chappell. M. 115, Pn., r.h., chord 1 has *sf* in Schott. Mm. 154, 155, 156, and 157, Pn., l.h., single wavy slur drawn as two slurs in edition. M. 221, Fl., notes 3–4 have strokes in Schott. M. 225, Fl., notes 1–2 have strokes in Schott. M. 227, Fl., notes 5–6 have strokes in Schott. M. 229, Pn., r.h., note 1 is 16th note. M. 244, Fl. and Vn., notes 6–7 lack strokes in Chappell. M. 245, Fl., notes 1–2 have dots in Chappell. M. 250, Fl., notes 6–7 have dots in Chappell. M. 251, Fl., notes 1–2 lack strokes in Chappell. M. 279, Fl., note 1 lacks dot in Schott.

II. Poco adagio

M. 21, Pn., r.h., between notes 13 and 14, turn symbol is missing in Chappell. Mm. 35, 42, and 44, Pn., l.h., single wavy slur drawn as two slurs in edition. Mm. 45 and 47, Vc., notes 2–10 have dots in Schott. Mm. 64–65, Pn., r.h. and l.h., single wavy slur (extending through the first half of m. 65) drawn as three slurs in edition. M. 77, Fl., notes 1–4 have dots in Chappell.

III. Menuetto

M. 27, Fl. and Vn., note 1 is 16th note. M. 32 lacks repeat bar. Mm. 34–36, Vc., strokes in Schott.

IV. Finale: Presto

M. 7, Pn., r.h., chords 1–2 have strokes in Schott. Mm. 98 and 100, Pn., r.h., beat 1 lacks *sf* in Schott. M. 192, Pn., l.h., beat 1 lacks *fz* in Schott.

Notes

1. Cited in Robert Münster, "Authentische Tempi zu den sechs lezten Sinfonien W. A. Mozarts?" *Mozart-Jahrbuch* (1962/63): 189. "Härtel schickt mir von die (!) beiden Mozartischen Sinfonien, die ich für Schultz arrangiert und wovon die eine der Großfürstin und die andere Göthe dedicirt ist, nur ein Exemplar von jeder."

2. See Karl Benyovsky, *J. N. Hummel, Der Mensch und Künstler* (Bratislava: Eos, 1934), 229 (cited above in note 32 of the introduction).

3. Münster, "Authentische Tempi zu den sechs lezten Sinfonien W. A. Mozarts?" 191 ("so geschwind als es möglich ist").